best lesbian erotica 1997

selected and introduced
by Jewelle Gomez

edited by
Tristan Taormino

CLEIS
PRESS

PRAISE FOR
BEST LESBIAN EROTICA 1996

"*Best Lesbian Erotica 1996* is by far the most innovative anthology of erotica I've seen...Roseanne Barr-style, no holds barred fiction [that] challenges every stereotyped view you might have had of lesbian erotica."
—Michael Perkins, author, *The Secret Record: Modern Erotic Literature*

"These women are looking for the edge and they find it."
—*Harvard Gay & Lesbian Review*

"Expect the unexpected in *Best Lesbian Erotica 1996...*"
—*Paramour Magazine*

Published in the United States by Cleis Press Inc., P.O. Box 8933, Pittsburgh, Pennsylvania 15221, and P.O. Box 14684, San Francisco, California 94114.

Printed in the United States.
Cover design: Scott Idleman / Blink
Interior design: Frank Wiedemann
Logo art: Juana Alicia
First Edition.
10 9 8 7 6 5 4 3 2 1

"Goddess Love" © by Katya Andreevna first appeared in *The New Worlds of Women* edited by Cecilia Tan (Cambridge, MA: Circlet Press, 1996). "Lay Lady Lay" © Red Jordan Arobateau is an excerpt from the novel *Lay Lady Lay* (Oakland, CA: Red Jordan Press, 1991). "Candy calls Star to her" © by Cheryl Clarke is an excerpt of the poem "Epic of Song" from the book *Humid Pitch* by Cheryl Clarke (Ithaca, NY: Firebrand Books, 1989). Reprinted by permission of Firebrand Books. "Against" © by Chrystos was published in *In Her I Am* by Chrystos (Press Gang Publishers, 1993). "L'Chiam, Mi Vida" © by Sandra Lee Golvin first appeared in *Pucker Up* #2 (1996) and is an excerpt of her novel-in-progress *Speaking the Language of the Dead*. "Flying Dreams" © by Raven B. Kaldera first appeared in *The New Worlds of Women* edited by Cecilia Tan (Cambridge, MA: Circlet Press, 1996). "After the Bath" © by Jenifer Levin was originally published in *Love and Death & Other Disasters* by Jenifer Levin (Ithaca, NY: Firebrand Books, 1996). Reprinted by permission of Firebrand Books. "Wives" © by Heather Lewis first appeared in *Surface Tension* edited by Meg Daly (New York: Simon & Schuster, 1996). "Credo" © by Cherríe Moraga was originally published in *The Last Generation* by Cherríe Moraga (Boston: South End Press, 1993). Reprinted by permission of the author and South End Press. "The Gateway" © by Kathleen E. Morris from *Speaking in Whispers: African-American Lesbian Erotica* by Kathleen E. Morris (Chicago: Third Side Press, 1996). Reprinted by permission of Third Side Press, Inc. "Julio" © by Mickey Laskin will be published in *Leatherwomen III* edited by Laura Antoniou (New York: Masquerade Books, forthcoming). "Ariel" © by Carol Queen is from her novel-in-progress, *The Leather Daddy and the Femme* (Pittsburgh: Cleis Press, forthcoming). "D & D" © by Kitty Tsui was originally published in *Breathless* by Kitty Tsui (Ithaca, NY: Firebrand Books, 1996). Reprinted by permission of Firebrand Books.

ACKNOWLEDGMENTS

To everyone at Cleis Press—especially Frédérique Delacoste, Felice Newman, Leasa Burton, and Deborah Barkun; they make it a pleasure to work with them everyday. To Jewelle Gomez for her hard work, her insight, and her convictions.

To Nancy Bereano of Firebrand Books, Steve Chase of South End Press, and Midge Stocker of Third Side Press for their support of the book and their assistance in securing permissions. To Meg Daly, Cecilia Tan, and Terry Wolverton for nominating various stories from anthologies they edited. To Enid Farber for her wonderful photograph on the cover.

To all the talented contributors of *Best Lesbian Erotica 1996* whose work and energy made our debut incredibly successful. Likewise, to the folks at A Different Light, Bodecia's Books, Barnes & Noble, Tower Books, and Meow Mix who gave overwhelming support to the first collection. To Heather Lewis, who constantly surpasses my expectations for a mentor, writer, teacher, and friend—her contributions have been invaluable.

To the following people who consistently offer me love, inspiration, and tremendous support: Kate Bornstein, Michelle Duff, Gerry Gomez Pearlberg, Kate Lambert, Robin Podolsky, Audrey Prins-Patt, my mother Judith Pynchon, Anna Lisa Suid McMorrow, D. Travers Scott, Linda Smukler, Jill Muir Sukenick, the memory of my father Bill Taormino, Riki Anne Wilchins, and Winston Wilde.

And, finally, to Karen Green, whose love brings me so much every single day.

CONTENTS

FOREWORD

When one lover leaves and another takes her place, a lot can change. You may start to socialize in new places, make new friends, take trips to different faraway places, even sleep on the other side of the bed. And what happens when you're *in* bed can transform too. The kisses are new, her touch feels different, her body and the energy between you exciting. There seems to be a whole new world out there to investigate. Or maybe you're just looking at it with different eyes.

After Heather Lewis and I finished *Best Lesbian Erotica 1996,* I paired with Jewelle Gomez to begin work on the 1997 book. Jewelle was up front about how she wanted to shape the collection she would select and introduce—she wanted to emphasize writing by and about women of color. So, I was faced with new questions. Instead of "What is lesbian erotica?" or "What is the state of erotic writing?" I confronted some more difficult queries. How do I, a white woman, thoughtfully solicit and edit submissions that focus on women of color? How do I talk about the politics and erotics of race and ethnicity in a meaningful way?

Putting together this collection and attempting to answer some of these questions has been challenging, frustrating, and enlightening. It has led me to re-examine the absence of specific voices and stories in mainstream erotica and re-think my own decisions as an editor. I began to seek out writing in new places, meet new groups of writers, and read submissions that delved into radically different territory than the past collection. I found myself expanding my own erotic palate in the process.

I met photographer Enid Farber, whose work appears on the cover, at a reading of *Best Lesbian Erotica 1996*. Later, when she showed me her portfolio, I was struck by a particular series of photos that documented a short-lived lesbian strip club by and for African-American and Latina women in the Washington Heights section of Manhattan. The images were raw, uninhibited, and sexy. They captured dancers getting ready backstage, strutting their stuff, flirting with customers. Farber caught a kiss between a dancer and the club's bouncer, a bunch of bills exchanged between voyeur and performer, and lots of heat between women. The picture may sound like a night at a typical strip club, but the goal of this club was not heteromale white-bread entertainment or great financial success; rather, it was a showcase and celebration of lesbian sex by and for women.

At a different club in Manhattan, lounge-lizard drag kings mix with leatherclad gender icons and slinky drag queens. Girls who look like fresh-faced boys flirt with boys who look like glammed-up girls. It may be simply the shadowy lighting, but you really can't tell anyone's gender for sure. Club Casanova, the world's first dyke drag-king club, is where I encountered many thought-provoking erotic images, and one interesting one in particular. S/he's a drag-king go-go dancer called Rabbi Schlomo Schlong dressed as—you guessed it—a Hasidic Jewish rabbi, complete with a starched white tse tse, long braids dangling out of the front of a black wide-brimmed hat, and a huge dick protruding from modest black pants.

When I first laid eyes on the Rabbi sensually gyrating to the music, grinding up against another go-go boy, grabbing the bulge between his/her legs, I admit I was shocked. Sort of offended. Definitely intrigued. My friends were surprised at my response; they were under the impression that, in the world of gender-bending, transgressive sexuality, and bizarre fetishes, nothing ruffled my feathers. I live in a neighborhood in Brooklyn that is divided into three distinct sections populated by Eastern European immigrants, Latino families and Hasidim. I walk on the street, go to the bank, and ride the subway with Hasidim everyday. I've never considered Hasidic men or rabbis erotic objects. But there was something about this dyke, who chose this particular sacred-symbol-cum-sex-object that made my skin burn and my heart race.

These two experiences epitomize what the writers in this anthology accomplish: they bring a variety of class, cultural, ethnic and racial identities and imagery into the landscape of erotic iconography. Ultimately, our identities have always been intertwined with our erotic lives; yet, mainstream sexual imagery often ignores our complexities. The majority of popular erotic representations excludes non-WASPs, poor and working-class people, and stories not part of the current status quo. Or they rely on one-dimensional stereotypes that are colonialist, exoticized, or sexist. In general, much of current erotica fails to fully examine how our individual backgrounds, cultures, and spirits relate to our intimate fantasies and forays.

The stories in this collection are about forging new erotic terrain. Not in a pale, let's-celebrate-difference kind of way, but through enticing journeys full of intriguing characters, compelling circumstances, and faraway places (that could be right next door). There are some very specific themes that characterize these tales: Moments of sacred initiation and sometimes sacrilegious ritual. Other-worldly encounters and excursions into the erotic imagination. Intricate psychological dynamics, which fuel intense, visceral desire. And uninhibited, slippery, passionate sex. Now, not all these stories have disregarded the submissive Asian girls, rough Latina gangsta-dykes, goddess-like African-American queens, and hard-working peep show girls; instead, they flesh out these superficial caricatures, turn them on their heads, or imagine complex new characters beyond simplistic stereotypes.

So leave your assumptions at the front door/cover, and delve into the rich territory the contributors have traveled and laid out for you. I promise you won't be disappointed.

Tristan Taormino
October 1996

introduction

To consider selecting "the best" of anything is, of course, to consider the impossible, since—like beauty—"best" is in the eye of the beholder. Even more daunting is the concept of best erotica. It immediately conjures up the word *naked*. Not just as in "breast" and "butt," that's fairly easy to contemplate, but "naked" as in exposing our needs and vulnerabilities. Since I do the choosing, I guess this is where I get naked.

In 1964, when my best friend and I first made love, we had little idea of the political ramifications of that moment when our nightgowns were cast down to the foot of the bed and our lips touched. We thought only of the immediate fear and joy; and then of the nights, every other Thursday, when my great-grandmother left us alone. We were just two black girls who laughed and joked together on the way to school, and then one day we were *LOVERS*. We had no way of understanding what has since become the cornerstone of the feminist movement: the personal is political. Our desire, and our acting on that desire, even when unarticulated, had a political impact on us individually and on the world around us. Much later I understood that there was a unique value to connecting with another like myself. I saw that in making that connection I began to have some control over my own life.

It was twenty years later that I found myself having to make that connection all over again. During the nineteen-eighties, when conservative feminists attacked our basic right to sexually explicit expression, it again became clear that such expression is at the core of women's liberation. Despite how women are terrorized daily in the home, on the street, in the media, women must demand our sexual desire be celebrated not veiled or reviled. We must continue to question exploitative modes of sexual expression while we actively support the basic right of sexual expression. The development of consciously explicit lesbian erotica has been a valuable balancing of the scales.

People like Jesse Helms and other conservatives found a new foothold in politics with the issue of pornography as framed by conservative feminists. And again, lesbians were the first to feel the noose as it tightened. While the debate is scarcely covered in the pages of our own publications today, the fight against repression continues. Little Sister's Bookstore in Canada has been fighting against obscenity charges for far too long and with far too little help. Feminist publishers are still being told by printers some work is too explicit or too lesbian to be printed. The large corporate publishers who churn out porn for the masses are not the ones who pay. It is those on the margins—lesbians, women, people of color—who are forced to justify our sexual desire.

The result has been an "asexualization" of lesbians in the popular media and a less than elementary discussion of the political ramifications of lesbian desire in most lesbian publications. We may now have the opportunity to be high-heeled, suited, glamorous, grubby, pierced and/or parenting in our own glossy magazines. But given that privilege, what do we mean to say about our desire, about the politics of our passion? How comfortable should we be when more and more often it is conservative lesbians and gays who are setting our political agenda in our communities and in Washington?

In revealing my own personal taste in lesbian erotica I know that I am also revealing my political beliefs about class, race, victimization, women's rights—about everything. I leafed through the selections understanding that many lesbians in this country don't have, as I do, the luxury of being completely out. Having a prime-time television movie made about the horror of her child being taken away from her because she has a lesbian lover did not get Sharon Bottoms custody of her son. Having lesbian parity in lesbian and gay film festivals doesn't save kids from being institutionalized by parents who are suspicious of their sexuality. We must be wary of confusing attention with progress.

The articulation of our desire is important but it does not happen in a vacuum. Behind our desire, behind the explicit voice we bring is the implication that we can all eventually take control of our lives. That is the horizon our stories point us toward.

I always try to keep in mind the women who are still struggling for their voices, so that I don't become too comfortable in my own life, too forgetful about the rest of the community. Because writing is about community. Telling our stories to each other, not just to take center stage, but to find understanding, to pass down history, to open up new paths for others. And for ourselves.

For me as a black lesbian, to pick stories and poems embodying lesbian desire, knowing that they will be published in a book sold in bookstores around the country, not under the counter but on the shelves—this remains a most political act. It is akin to reaching out that first time to touch my best friend's body. This is a country where African Americans have fought to be allowed the right to read, where women of color are still routinely victimized by media misrepresentation, where our sexuality is used against us. The sexual stereotypes about women of color still abound and not just on television and movies but (because we are raised in the same county of "isms" as every one else) also in lesbian bars, businesses and activist organizations. When we are seen at all it is often only as objects—colorful, comic, exotic, both comforting and threatening. Facing the most obviously misguided assumptions every day, lesbians of color still insist upon reaching out, on participating in the lesbian community and the world of lesbian erotic writing. It is as Audre Lorde has counselled: "our silence will not save us."

In choosing these pieces I thought about the years we were encouraged to embrace silence while at the very same time so many lesbians still managed to stir our erotic imaginations. In 1927, when *The Well of Loneliness* was banned from publication in the United States, it was the erotic potential of that novel (probably made even more potent because it was so repressed) that disturbed censors. Writers such as Radclyffe Hall, and later Ann Bannon and Ann Allen Schockley, helped create the place for our desire. But they could never have anticipated just how sensuous, eclectic, transgressive or romantic a space contemporary lesbians would create in literature. Yet we are all connected. They cut the path that young lesbian writers are now broadening.

Those travelling that road in this collection will cover such large territory it's impossible to sketch it out and do justice to the unique quality of each writer. Suffice it to say that the book includes the rawness of veteran erotica writer, Red Jordan Arobateau ("Lay Lady Lay"), the edgy quality of Karen Green ("The Wall of Unsaid Things"), the freshness of Donna Allegra ("Bread from a Stone"), and the penetrating (literally) spark of Cecilia Tan ("Penetration"). The life of the imagination has never been livelier as when, in "The Gateway," Kathleen E. Morris's "buppy" lesbian explores the possibility that visitors to Earth from beyond the stars are not little green men. Or when Robin Bernstein evokes the yearning for acceptance a young girl experiences when she visits a Jewish bookstore searching for a gift for her lover in "Virgin's Gift."

In addition to fiction, I've included some poetry because it is so much a part of the development of the lesbian oral tradition. During the early days of the lesbian-feminist movement, love poems were a staple of any political or literary event. Over the years, the writers who've developed their skills in the lesbian context, such as Adrienne Rich, Audre Lorde or Marilyn Hacker, have set the standard for all erotic poetry in this country. The poets included here—Cheryl Clarke ("Candy calls Star to her"), Cherríe Moraga ("Credo"), Chrystos ("Against")—have the distinction of also being activists in the lesbian community as well as in their own ethnic communities. In the erotic texture and text of their work, I think we see the full spectrum of who lesbians have been and can be. And we see that the political mind does not have to be a dry mind!

The pieces here are a chorus of voices, each one embodying desire in different ways, and helping to dispel the silence the larger society would like to spread so tightly over us. These stories and poems build on our history of repression as well as our history of joy and triumph. And it is in their radically eclectic depiction of lesbian desire that their power lives. When we are able to accept the difference between our stories, between each of us, when we can appreciate those differences or simply support them, we open ourselves to the possibilities of new erotic experience and help form a bond with each other. And every healthy connection with another woman is a political advantage.

Whether you've got a fetish for boots, bubble bath or big women, dildos, goddesses or just romance, there are words in here for you. Words that help define our community, teach us lessons for survival, and make us wet.

Jewelle Gomez
October 1996

credo

CHERRÍE MORAGA

Frente al altar de mi madre
burning beds
de lagrimas cling
to the frozen face
of glass, flame quaking
in the wake
of the meeting
of mothers.

Tenemos el mismo problema,
the one says to the other
sin saber the meaning.

Each, their youngest daughter
a heretic
a non-believer.

But when you raised the burning
bush of cedar
our faces twin moons in the black night
I believed and dreamed
my body stripped naked
like the virgin daughter
splayed upon your altar.

Not that you, my priestess
would wrench from me
my heart sangrando
but to feel your hand heavy
on that raised hill
of flesh

my breast
rising

like a pyramid
from the sacred
walls of templo

my body.

The Boot Wall

Dawn Milton

Ann stood at the kitchen counter with the phone to her ear. Her eyes gazed through the window and settled on a small brown bird perched on a bush at the far corner of the backyard. The bush bobbed up and down in the wind, but the bird kept its grip. Flat gray bellies of clouds rolled in overhead, beckoning a thick spring rainstorm. She hoped it would pour.

"...won't be back until late," the man at the other end was saying. His voice had that strained sound that always came with anger. Like he was strangling something while continuing to speak through clamped teeth. The result was a gruff half-whisper that felt like a shout. An uncompromising order.

"You will make yourselves dinner. Read your Bibles and do your homework. See to it that Ben puts the guitar away. And I don't need to remind you that you will *not* be on the phone again. I will not tell you twice. Is that clear?"

"Yes, that's clear," she answered, trying to execute a safe sarcasm, a touch of resistance.

"What?" A whip-crack back at her. No room for smart talk.

"It's clear, Daddy. I heard you," she managed, finally.

There was a click and the dull hum of the dial tone. He never said good-bye when he was angry.

"Son-of-a-bitch. Dammit!" She dropped the handset on the counter, watched it noisily roll back and forth.

Ann leaned her stomach into the edge of the counter until she could feel the Formica biting into her skin. The fingers of her left hand were white from having wound the cord around them so tight. She didn't need reminding about the phone. Her father had forbidden her to use it for the last four weeks, since the day she had forged his ragged signature on a note and got caught ditching school with Adrian. Her "phone privileges" had been lost for two months, along with her spare time and the freedom she had only recently begun to discover in friendships. Since then he left for the construction site at four or five in the morning so that most days he could be back by the time she walked home from school. He would leave the job early and hit the freeway before rush hour, just so he could ensure that she was effectively disciplined with silence, structure and the Bible. Mostly though, it seemed to be about keeping an eye on her and Ben, making sure they did not stray any further.

He never hit her, or touched her in the wrong places, or yelled at her. He saved the belt-spankings for Ben, whose misbehavior came more often, or at least was more obvious. He reserved for Ann a style of punishment that refused to yield any such vulnerability on his part. Had he raised his voice, he might have revealed a fissure, a crack of pain that his daughter was fifteen years old and he was finally losing her, like he figured he eventually would. It had been six years since he won custody, and the choice to leave had been hers from the time she was twelve, but she wasn't ready to do that. Maybe next year she would move to her mother's house, an hour north on the 405 freeway. For now, it was too important to hold onto the friends she had finally managed to find in this well-groomed Southern California suburb that was so different from the gritty mountain town where they had all lived before the divorce. Her hold on her life here felt tenuous enough; she could never match the things the golden-haired kids had, or be allowed to kill time like they did, or even watch TV with them in her own house. He hated television as much as he hated phones, so they didn't own one. She was not allowed to drive any of his three cars, and he did hadn't offered to teach her anyway—like a lot of things, he left that to Celine, her mother.

The phone seemed to bother him the most. Even before he grounded her, he had gone out of his way to contain its threat. They were not allowed to make calls in the mornings before school. No calls between five and seven in the evening, the part of the day he called suppertime, though they only occasionally ate on that schedule. No phone on Sunday, the Lord's day. And no calls over ten minutes long. When she or Ben did get a call that he answered, he'd hand the phone over with pursed lips, like they'd done something wrong. He could barely manage a stern "hello." As a result, most of their friends didn't call unless they knew he was gone, or they absolutely had to say something, which wasn't that often. As her friends figured out, and as Ann was sure he was trying to prove, most things could usually wait until tomorrow. But the silence made the stricture that much more hollow. The evenings where the only sound came from the thin crinkle of the pages of his Bible being turned were long and eerie. And bedroom doors were not allowed to be closed until bedtime—so that he could see that they were studying or reading. Sometimes she and Ben would go into one of their rooms and talk quietly, but Ben, these days, was usually hiding inside his science-fiction stories or needling endlessly on his guitar, and, with doors always open, the conversations never felt free.

Ann had begun to figure out in the last month of her "restriction" (as he liked to call it) that there was an edge to her father's silence that matched the gruffness in his voice. Maybe it was the sadness that she had come to recognize so easily during the custody battles—the burning-eyes sadness, the grief that brought him to barely whispered good-byes on weekends when he'd drop them back off at their mother's after a visit with him. He was eventually awarded custody, to her mother's frustration and despair, by a judge who sympathized with his anger toward his wife for not loving him and who had the power to prove it. That was six years ago. The old sadness had retreated since that victory, yet it still lurked behind his pale blue eyes.

But the edge was not just that. And it was not just the strictness he bore like a proud burden—the cross of his stubborn work ethic. He still had to prove to the world that he was raised by poor farmers in Iowa, who had none of these modern conveniences and were better for it. He had been waking up at four a.m. since he could remember, and his parents, he would remind his children, would surely have whipped him if he'd in any way refused to cooperate. The strictness itself was not the edge, though—there was something underneath it. A protective meanness. And poison—like a scorpion guarding its young, its tail up and rattling. It had been in his voice tonight when he had to call twice, because the first time the phone had been busy.

It was three-thirty when Ann had come in the door. The phone was ringing when she walked in. She ran to catch it. It was Adrian. Ann felt her gut drop. Lately, she could not get enough of Adrian, the new girl she had made friends with at the beginning of the year. Tall, strong and direct, Adrian was the kind of jock who was quiet and withdrawn everywhere but the court or the playing field. There was no bullshit about her, and she recoiled at the rich kids at the high school as much as Ann did. Recently, they had begun hanging out by themselves at the far edge of the softball field during lunch, talking about where they'd come from and where they hoped to go.

"Ad, you know I can't talk. My dad's gonna be home any minute."

"I know, I know," Adrian said. "But I wanted to remind you to bring shorts and sneakers to school tomorrow. That rally thing is happening and we have to beat those stupid cheerleaders in the tug-of-war. It'll be the highlight of your day." Adrian rarely participated in the social activities going on at school, but cheerleaders annoyed her enough to bring her out for this event.

"Okay, I'll remember. I'll see you in the morning."

As soon as she hung up, the phone had rung again and it was her father, fiercely angry that he'd gotten the busy signal. Of course, he hadn't waited for or wanted an explanation. There was no explanation that would make it right for him. It was cut and dry: she had disobeyed. "Children, obey your parents"—a Biblical commandment—and, for him, about as clear as you could get. The furious hiss of his voice still echoed in her brain.

The rain was splattering against perfectly green lawns as Ann strode into the master bedroom, cheeks still flaming from the phone call. Ben was not home yet, probably out somewhere at a friend's house, cherishing free afternoons for as long as he could hold onto them until the next grounding. The only sound was the wallop of water coming down hard now against the shingled roof, a crashing that couldn't drown out the heavy breaths of her frustration. She kept pacing back and forth across the open doorway, in and out of her father's room.

She wasn't sure what brought her into his room. She would have gone outside or down a few streets to Adrian's but, surely, if she did that, he would have called again and gotten no answer, and that would be worse than getting caught on the phone. So she walked in circles with her hands pressed against her forehead, talking back in her head to the man whose walls she could never penetrate. His specialty as a carpenter was framing; he spent his life building strong walls. She stood in the room, cursing the man she could never talk back to in real life.

She cursed his voice, she cursed his face, she cursed his anger. She cursed his Iowa, his sucked-dry, stiff-necked family, and his thousand different jobs, his four a.m. departures and his afternoon arrivals. She cursed the I-love-you's he rained on Ben and her when he was in a good mood, and she cursed the ways he made it hard for them to love him back and mean it anymore. She cursed him for moving them to Southern California and trying to make them live a small-town life there, in the midst of luxury and wealth and modernness. She cursed the Cadillac and the 1956 Lincoln Continental that he spent weekends hovering over, while he drove a battered old van to and from work. She cursed the out-of-place Western wear he wore, with his Stetsons and belt buckles and leather sport coats and cowboy boots. "God, the guy wears cowboy boots in Newport Beach," she muttered.

At this thought, Ann looked up at the wall across from her, the wall where he kept his boots. Her father had spent a few years of his life ranching when he was in his twenties, and, aside from his spectator tours of the national rodeo circuit, the style of his wardrobe was the only thing that remained of his cowboy past. Never returning to that life was a loss he rarely admitted, but, like most things, Ann could see it in his eyes. He was a nineteen-forties' Marlboro man caught in a nineteen-eighties' world of smoggy, sprawling Metropoles, but only half-searching for a way back to Big Sky country. He knew how to make money in construction and there was a lot of construction in Southern California. Sometimes he schemed out loud about buying a ranch and moving to Montana or Wyoming. He would drive them through miles of cattle grazing property in the summers, sometimes stopping to check on the price of land, but the move never happened.

The loss of the dream was reflected in the things he bought and wore. On the wall facing Ann he had built a series of shelves, stacked from the floor to almost the ceiling. They took up about an eight-foot space between the bedroom doors and the closet. Each shelf supported a line of cowboy boots, most of them cut from exotic leather, six pair to a shelf, neatly placed with the toes pointing into the room. He kept them in order: workboots and old boots at the bottom, regular dress boots (for church and social occasions) on the middle shelves, fancy ones toward the top. An old shoe horse he had built sat in front of the display, hung with boot rags, stained burgundy and black from shoe polish.

Ann scanned the shelves and a shudder went through her. Suddenly she wanted to run to the bathroom and throw up but she couldn't move her feet.

When she was younger, she used to stand with him and name the animals whose skins provided his boot collection. She remembered most of the purchases specifically, since she and Ben had spent long hours watching him try on boots every year in Cheyenne when he took them to the rodeo. The trips to Frontier Days were their father's only personal shopping expeditions of the year, but when he did it, he did it big. Months in advance, the clerks at the store would special order boots they thought he would like, making sure they always had size nine and a half, A-width. He owned boots of tortoiseskin, frogskin, crocodile and several variations of lizard. Boa-constrictor, in both regular style and back-cut so the scales flipped up. Elephant boots, rough gray with deep, beautiful wrinkles, and kangaroo boots, softer than antelope or calfskin. There were several different toe styles, and boots with fancy, custom stitched tops in multi-colored threads—Lucheses, Dan Posts, Durangos, Larry Mahans, Justins. No pair was the same, and they always drew comments from surprised neighbors and people in grocery stores.

"Fancy cowboy boots you got there," they would say in a bad attempt at a Western accent as they stood in the checkout line in their Cole Haan penny loafers, smiling fakely, hoping for some explanation.

"Thank you, Sir (or Ma'am)," he'd say, proving his foreignness by the inflection, like some new-to-town stranger in a dusty Western. He'd answer in just such a way that they wouldn't ask anything else, except maybe what kind of leather they were. They'd scan him from the boots up, eyeing his Wranglers, his huge gold and silver belt buckle, his western floral-print shirt and custom-made, ten-gallon hat. They'd glance at Ann and Ben, and then, unsatisfied but awkward against his silence, back to their groceries.

Her father wore his cowboy boots, belt buckles and hats with just the slightest edge of pride, the kind of pride Ann recognized as dangerous, in the Biblical sense. It wasn't boastful or haughty, exactly, but there was something swollen about it. She'd seen it in his eyes over the years, when he sauntered back and forth in the Ranchman Outfitters in Cheyenne, working in the leather on some antelope boots he was considering.

"You like 'em, Muffit?" he'd ask her, as the salespeople looked on.

"Sure, Daddy, they're pretty," she would reply, waiting until they could get back to the hotel where she and Ben could wash off the fairground dirt in the pool. He never bought boots for them—he said they would grow out of them too soon and it'd be a waste of money. Which was okay, since the only time she ever wanted cowboy boots was one week a year, sitting in that store in Wyoming, gazing down the aisles of shining leather. The rest of the time she wouldn't be caught dead dressing like him. Besides, she'd've been laughed out of school if she had.

Now she looked at the rows of boots on his shelves and they pointed back at her, a stoic arsenal of leather arrows. "Thou Shall Not Covet," she thought. And then, impulsively, she grabbed a pair directly across from her, pinching the tops together, and walked with them further into the room, where his bed and dresser were. At the sight of the dresser, she plunked the boots onto the carpet and sat on the bed, looking at the contents on the dresser top.

There were buffalo nickels and half-dollars and Susan B. Anthonys in an old ashtray covered in a thin layer of dust. The kind of collection a boy would keep, but interspersed with adult paraphernalia. Plain money clips with two dollar bills in them, and money clips that were just for the wearing, studded with bits of turquoise and coral. There was a bolo tie he saved for the rare occasions when he dressed up and went to a restaurant show with his friends from his old bar business. A blue tiger's eye sapphire ring set in platinum which he usually wore on his little finger, but not when he was hammering nails, like tonight. An old, black and white picture of the back of him riding Raincheck, the Appaloosa he kept when they lived in the mountains, but had to sell after the divorce. The three of them used to go riding on him, Ben in front of his father, Ann straddled just behind the saddle on the horse's hindquarters. None of them had ridden in years. There was a framed picture of the three of them at the rodeo in 1976, taken when she was ten and Ben was eight. They were both proudly wearing the red-white-and-blue leather Bicentennial jackets their dad had bought them. It was one of the rare occasions where he'd dressed his children as ornately as he dressed himself.

Next to the picture was one of his gaudiest buckles. It was his favorite—a huge gold and silver number in the rounded square shape of saddle bronc-riding trophy buckles. But he had not won the buckle, of course—he'd had it custom made by a jeweler friend from Texas who shared front row seats in the rodeo stands with the family every summer. He paid over one thousand dollars for it. Stamped across a gold ribbon in elaborate script were the words, *Jesus is Lord,* punctuated at the bottom of the *D* with a sparkling red ruby. A silver lasso wound around the edge of the buckle, framing his piety. The Fellowship of Christian Cowboys couldn't have asked for a prettier· buckle or a better representative.

Ann picked up the heavy piece of metal and passed it back and forth in her hands, feeling its solid weight. "Jesus is Lord," she thought. "And Daddy loves Jesus." Her heart started pounding in her chest. The rain on the roof echoed in the room.

She ran the fingers of one hand back and forth against the edges of the design, and felt the smooth, slightly arced back of the buckle. "Jesus is Lord, and the Lord speaks through Daddy," she whispered out loud. She pictured him guiding the wide, tooled-leather belt through his belt loops, watching the mirror as he fitted the buckle into the notch, getting ready to go out. He liked to go out dancing during rodeo vacations. He always wore his best for that and walked tall, his buckle gleaming as he strolled down the halls of the Little America Hotel in Cheyenne, where all the country-music acts stayed, and a lot of the cowboys. She and Ben would lean out the hotel-room door and watch him go, then flop on the big beds and watch TV for hours while he was gone.

Then she remembered the times he whipped that belt out of the loops to give Ben a spanking, the boy bent over, braced; the man poised, controlled, accurate and quick. The ritual words, "Son, this hurts me more than it hurts you." The way distance would grow between them after that intimate act. He would always speak in a quiet voice, afterwards. Ben wouldn't speak at all.

Some boundaries were crossed and others were never even attempted in this house. Ann felt herself facing a barbed-wire fence in her mind and wanted to slip through. She looked down at the boots on the floor next to her and knew she was about to trespass. She couldn't see the movement yet but felt it coming, like the distant ricketing of a train gliding across a long prairie. Her legs quivered.

She was rocking slowly on the bed now. She felt the weight of her body, her presence in his room. "Daddy hates the phone," she muttered. "So Jesus hates the phone." Her head was beginning to fill with images, quick and layered, overlapping.

She dropped the buckle on her lap, felt the metal slide sideways against her Levi's and between her thighs onto the mattress. The cool weight was good there. She pressed her legs together, making the metal bite into the crotch seam of her jeans. *It will be this way,* she thought, suddenly. *And he will never know.* She flashed on Adrian, her hands gripped to the tug-of-war rope, pulling screaming cheerleaders across the line. She, too, started pulling.

She heard again his gruff voice on the phone. "I will not tell you twice..." She saw the stubborn set of his tan, whiskered jaw. The finality of his words.

"Jesus speaks through Daddy." She was mocking now, her voice louder. "And Jesus is always right. 'You don't question the Lord.' " She mimicked his sternness. Pushed herself against the buckle, harder now.

She leaned over and picked up the boots from where she had left them on the floor. They were made of eelskin. The leather was stitched in strips running diagonally across the foot of the boot, from the pointed toe, across the top, and around the heel. The skin was slick, shiny and black as pitch. Her fingers, sweating, pressed sticky prints into the glossy leather. She put the sole of one boot on each thigh, so they were standing on her legs, the tops of them almost to her chin as she sat on the bed. She dropped her head forward and breathed deeply of the boot.

Closing her eyes, she could see the aisles in the boot store and smell the overwhelming press of leather—calfskin; buckskin; the hard, thick hide of belts; the sweet, cottony pelt of sheepskin, where she used to bury her face in the linings of the big coats. She inhaled from one boot and then the other, smelling cattle, fences, earth, grassy ranch land. She rubbed the palms of her hands up and down the slick tops to the tight angle of the toes, smelling Kiwi shoe polish. She remembered polishing his boots with him, the feel of the soft bristle brushes, buff pads, and buckskin chamois, the whipping of cloth across the leather. The "thhck, thhck" dry slapping sound it made.

She flopped backwards onto the bed, the boots still standing on her thighs, the buckle pressing against her crotch. "Jesus," she whispered, and a collage of visions flashed through her mind. She saw a young, tanned man wearing leather sandals, his body draped in a sandy cloth, running his hands down the trunk of a gnarled olive tree, waiting. Then another carpenter, an old man with white hair in faded Wranglers and a T-shirt, hoisting the pine skeleton of a wall before him to stand it vertically. The crack of a twenty-pound hammer on a five-penny nail. Slick rain sliding down the bright white walls of Jerusalem. Old men hunched in black robes, pressing paper prayers between the crevices of huge stones at the Wailing Wall. The thunder of wild Mustangs. Jesus is coming.

This is how it will happen. She rode the images, pushing against the hard metal buckle, digging her fingernails into the seams at the tops of the boots. *On his things,* she thought, *these are his things.* She ran one hand under her pants so that the buckle was pressed between one palm on the outside of her jeans and one on the inside. She arched into the hard silver. *Fuck you, Daddy.*

Her hands were erratic now. She ran one under her T-shirt and unsnapped her bra at the breastbone. With the other, she pulled open the front of her jeans, feeling the buttons pop free, and slid the buckle into her underpants, past her pubic mound and down to the slick place between her labia. She had to spread her legs wide to rub the broad side, the "Jesus is Lord" side, against her, and she felt the pressure in her, a cumulous cloud, fast and warm. She tipped one boot back and ran the length of it across her belly and between her breasts. She moved the top of the boot across her chest, felt the seams in the eelskin slide over her nipples. She kept this boot moving roughly over her and pointed the other down to her crotch. There she pushed the tip of the toe into her underwear against her, the leather cool next to her skin.

Her jeans were halfway down her legs now, her cotton underpants stretched taut across her thighs. Squeezing her legs together against the friction of the huge buckle, she moved back and forth across it, covering it with melting slickness. The toe of the boot pressed into her clit, knocking against the edge of the buckle at the same time. She rocked fast and hard, loving the difference between the metal and the black leather.

This is it, she thought, breathing hard. *And you will never catch me.*

The rain pounded against the roof, unrelenting. She heard hammering, steel hitting iron. She watched Jesus walking down the path, between olive trees, his sandals barely skimming the ground. She saw Adrian, too. She saw the thick brown mud of the tug-of-war pit, watched the girls dig their heels into it as they fought the drag of the rope in Adrian's hands, pulling them into the mud. She arched into the boot, staining it blacker with her wetness. She ground against the silver, pressed it hard. She felt the pounding of hoofs, the roar of a stampede getting closer. She came yelling. She came angry. The explosion thundered on all sides of her, deafening and chaotic.

She heaved until the breaths came more evenly and then she cried, leaning into the persistent sound of the rain. After awhile, when the roar inside her subsided, she sat up on the bed, buttoned her jeans and wiped the belt buckle across her T-shirt. She placed it back on the dresser.

The boots she slipped back into place on the boot wall, between the kangaroos and the elephants. She left them as they were, still glistening.

The First Time

LAURA ANTONIOU

The first time I was bound, she wound strips of a mutilated white cotton nightdress around each wrist, chiding me for my rude behavior. How dare I make fun of her exquisite gowns, delicately edged in lace, gathered slightly below the bodice and sweeping to cover my feet while floating above her own delicate ankles. I'd laughed at them, these gently worn, sensual garments of such feminine intensity that I could not even imagine them near my skin, unless they were clinging to her body, then pressed next to mine. But wear such a thing? No, not I.

When she picked up the scissors, I laughed aloud and shivered in mock fear. When she made the first cut, just below the neckline, I started to reach for her, to stop her from destroying such a pretty thing. But her arms tightened, and all the concentration in her eyes pinned me to the bed. I had to watch her rip through the thin cotton, making ragged, long tears that rapidly became strips of anonymous white material, ethereal yet stronger than I might have guessed.

I pulled one hand away, testing her fortitude, and she slapped me with an imperious look. It was delicious. I let her bring my hands together, wrapping them around with one strip, and then across with another; then I relaxed back onto her rich linen sheets and hand-embroidered pillowcases.

I let her touch me, smiling and sighing between the giggles, and reached for her as if to fight, aching for the strips to be tighter, to keep my hands above my head so there was no way I could impede her progress as she continued to make her points with maddeningly light slaps to my body. I reared up once, to kiss her, and she pushed me back as easily as I could push her slight body around and yes, I let her.

I wanted to see what she was going to do.

Because no one had bound me before.

But we were young and shy and the boldness we showed on stage and in the dark corners behind the scenery vanished into the awkwardness of authentic intimacy. She reared back herself, and during the silence, we both made our decisions. We were apart before long, and she remained a sharp reminder of the dangers of straight women, the perfidy of femmes. And she made me hunger for shadows of her for years, until at last I laid myself down for a woman in a gown, and sighed in perfect release and abandon.

Or, maybe it didn't happen that way at all, maybe I imagined it.

Because the first time I was bound, it was to my own bed, by a man younger than I; he was an aching, beautiful boy, expertly instructed and coached by the one who knew exactly what she wanted. He danced and ran and shook his body in delight, never still, never at repose, even when he snuggled up to me in the coldest moments of the night. He grinned when I sought his eyes and told him it was time, and he eagerly handled my toys and used them in careful progression, making me crazy with need and then falling on me with a passion so pure it had to be exactly as he claimed—virginal. We gave each other a sacrifice that year, cutting into ourselves and handing over the warm, moist parts that were our secret passions.

I bared myself for him, and he bared himself to me. He struck me with all his youthful strength, and crammed folded towels in my mouth to muffle the cries, and held onto me later, when his body twitched in a sleep without rest. He didn't tease, couldn't know how to tease, and so he satisfied me fully, and made me feel that I might actually have a way to fulfill this desperate need in me.

I knew precisely what he was going to do; I was his instructor.

I needed to be in charge; no one had ever bound me before.

And so he knew where the tools were, and knew exactly the kinds of stimulation I wanted, where, how often, for how long. I was in absolute control of my tender young faggot, my sweet lonely lover, and was able to surrender to my passions, if not to him.

Or maybe it didn't happen that way at all.

Because, really, the first time I was bound, it was by a stranger. A tall, powerful woman who could have lived my life twice with time to spare. She buckled worn, leather cuffs onto my wrists and locked them in place and slapped me, hard. I could not look at her while she completed the rituals that transformed her from the rough-voiced seducer in a crowded and smoky bar into the sleek, silken seductress who could charm the most frightened young woman into a very dangerous game. I knew the proper words to say and the proper games to play, but still I went with her to a place I did not know, leaving no one behind to call for me, or to know into whose hands I had given myself.

She stripped my body and tied me up tight, and for the first time, I truly felt the pull of restraints placed on me by another, the weight of my own body, the limits of my own strength. And she stroked my face tenderly before striking me again, and again, and kissed the blood from my teeth and lips, so I could see it on her when she drew away. In a too-late moment of indecision, I tested the bonds and found them locked onto me, impossible to slip or lift off. And I knew what it meant to be truly helpless, at another's mercy. Alone, with a person who was known for being merciless.

I had no idea what she was going to do.

I was terrified, because no one had ever bound me before.

She brought weapons before me—silky, dangerous weapons like herself—and let me be romanced by them before they launched into brutality. Opening my bruised mouth, she commanded words from me, and got only sounds, and her fury was so magnificent that I knew she was beyond human. She demanded worship. And in the end, she got it. At a price so great, I was never to see her again.

No, it didn't happen that way at all.

The first time I was bound, it was by words alone. "Stay there," and "stand still," and "don't move," uttered with a playful, casual simplicity, punctuated by stinging cuts, which threw ripples of distraction all along nerve endings. A light voice and soft hands, and a test that was designed for me to fail. I ground my teeth and set my body and keened lengthy screams that echoed in my skull but actually came out in hisses and gasps. And the more I obeyed, the harsher it was, until the agony exploded and waves of nausea swept through me. Drunkenly stubborn, I locked my limbs in place—I would stay there, stand still, and not move, until rivers of blood covered my body, until my lungs couldn't draw another breath, until the starbursts of pain behind my eyelids became one bright red light and I fell to the floor and didn't know anymore.

And I did fall, but not to the ground. Instead, I spiraled inward, and my obedience to the commands left my body no choice but to ignore those petty, spiteful stings. They faded into distant jabs, which distracted me from myself, and when they rose in a flurry of angry impotence, I ceased to mind them at all.

I didn't know what was happening.

I had never been bound before.

Not much later, hands beat against my locked arms and fingers and bent me forward and at last I moved, and the sizzling, crackling awakenings of my body finally made me cry out. I could barely hear him, cradling me, his once cynical voice trembling with shame and horror and fear, as he asked over and over again, why I had not moved. I knew then that he could hold me no longer, and so I let him soothe me, and did not remind him whose bonds had held me so fast. I knew that he hated me then, and I allowed that hate to fill me with much-belated pain, and freed myself minutes after he left me for the last time.

No, it couldn't have happened that way.

No, really, the first time I was bound it was after years and years of bondage, when I was handed two pairs of cuffs and told to put them on. When I passed under the bed legs the rope I cut the night before, and lay down in a genuine state of fear. Not of her, but fear that because I had never been bound, I shouldn't have been there, hadn't earned my way to that strange bed and those accurate hands.

And with the two items I had brought and the one she had, she taught me what it was like to be tied, to be spread so wide that there were no safe places on my body. She taught me that wherever I had gone before was not accessible through her, and when at last the tears came, I gave myself to them wholeheartedly, never losing myself, never turning away.

The cuffs were snug and light, and when I pulled against them, I did nothing but press my body wider for her. And in time, when I was turned and moved, it was her voice that held me and the bondage seemed almost superfluous. I struggled against the ties and sighed in agony as they refused to give, and in one blissful moment, reared against them, fingers curled and my entire body tensed to tear them from their anchor points. They held. What a luxury to be so tightly bound.

"Luxurious, ain't it?" she breathed into my ear.

And I cried again, clean tears that poured through me, soaking my face, my hair, the sheets beneath me, because I was so grateful for that moment.

You see, I'd never been bound before.

And when the bonds were gone, I found that they had stayed with me anyway, and I slept in them and wore them for quite some time. The marks were not to fade from my body for months, years maybe, but the cuffs are still there, waiting for the rope under the bed.

But maybe that wasn't the way it happened at all.

Maybe it's still to come.

The Gateway

KATHLEEN E. MORRIS

Something bright flashed in Patrice's peripheral vision. Curious, she backed up, peering into the bare, ice-covered branches of the bush but seeing nothing. Maybe it was just the sun reflecting off the ice, she decided as she continued her morning jog.

The next morning, Patrice ran with her friend, Linda. The air was cold, invigorating. The two women talked and laughed as they made their way down the deserted path. Patrice remembered the silver flash of yesterday, and as they came upon the bush, Patrice looked into the branches. The bush wavered like a mirage, almost translucent. Then, a sudden flash of silver. Patrice grabbed Linda's arm. "Did you see that?"

"What? See what?"

Patrice jogged over to the bush, reaching out a hand to touch the frozen branches. Gripping a twig, she watched the melting ice drip through her fingers.

"What's the matter? Hey—Pat!" Linda stopped beside Patrice, a look of concern on her face.

Patrice slowly withdrew her hand. "Ummm...nothing. It was nothing." Patrice smiled shakily. "I'll race you back to my place. Loser cooks breakfast!"

The following morning, Patrice started out a little earlier and reversed her route. Coming upon the bush, she saw a figure kneeling on the ground. It was difficult to determine whether the person was male or female, dressed as it was in a padded bodysuit, only the face visible. The face was dark, blue-black like the night, and flawless. As

Patrice came closer, the figure looked up and Patrice stopped in her tracks. The figure's eyes were a startling, vivid yellow. No pupils, just two glowing moons in a midnight face. The figure stood and, with a last look at the stunned Patrice, jumped into the bush.

Patrice waited a few seconds, but the creature did not reemerge, so she crept cautiously forward. Her heart was pounding as she moved closer, ready to run if there were any sudden movements. She peered into the bush. There was nothing there. Patrice walked around the bush. She saw footprints where the person had been, but none anywhere else. Despite the cold, Patrice broke into a sweat. She backed away down the path, not turning until the bush was no longer in sight. Then she ran like hell.

All day, Patrice contemplated the figure and the bush. What did it mean? She hesitated mentioning the experience—even to Linda—and risk being labeled a nut case with invitations to speak on talk shows. She needed incontrovertible proof. Of what? She didn't know. But she *had* to go back.

Patrice dressed warmly and left her house earlier than usual the next morning, her stride tense, cautious as she neared the park, camera slung around her neck. She felt ridiculous, like a bad actor in a B movie—the kind where the victim ignores her instincts to run as fast and as far away as possible without looking back, but instead continues on to her certain doom.

Sitting on a bench behind a tree not more than a hundred yards from the bush, Patrice waited. Before long, the bush began to waver. Patrice rubbed her eyes and stared as a person stepped out of the bush and looked around. Patrice ducked behind the tree, removing the cap from the lens of the camera. The figure turned and moved away from the bush, making notes on a silver board. Patrice started snapping pictures as the being moved about, studying and recording.

Patrice had to get closer. Sliding off the bench, Patrice inched around the tree. She stepped on a twig that snapped loudly in the cold, still air. The being turned, yellow orbs flashing. It looked to the bush, assessing the distance. Patrice made a sprint at the same moment, and when the being leapt into the bushes, so did Patrice. There was a flash of silver, and then blackness.

When she awoke, Patrice was strapped to a table in a darkened room. Taking careful inventory of her body, she assessed that she was not injured. "Stay calm," she chanted as her eyes adjusted to the gloom. She could make out that she was in some sort of examination room. Her head was held loosely in a vise, but by straining her eyes to the right, she could make out a large console with dim, blinking, blue lights pushed up against the wall. It was perhaps four feet from the table she lay on, with dark wires running from it to—to her!

Cutting her eyes to the left, she made out a monitor, silently printing out data received from the wires she could now feel attached to her pulse points.

She had to be dreaming. What had happened? She tried to recall her actions before the blackout. Jumping into the bushes—and then—here. Suddenly there was a blinding, painful flash of silver. Patrice screamed, and passed out.

When she came to again, the being was beside her, adjusting the wires, studying the printout. Through half-lidded eyes, Patrice studied it. About five-foot-eight, it was slim, even under the silver padded suit it wore. The skin was indeed blue-black, gleaming and ageless. And it was flawless—except for a silver geometric etching running from its right eye to its hawkish nose. Its lips were full, sharp and black. But the eyes were what drew Patrice. The eyes, framed by thick, silver brows and lashes, were luminescent, and Patrice gasped as she realized that the being's eyes were giving off the only light in the room.

There were no ornaments or designs on the uniform to give Patrice a clue as to where she might be. But she knew for damn sure, she wasn't in any hospital. And she knew that *it* was not human.

It turned to her. "Ah, Patrice, you are awake."

The voice was female. Soft, without inflection.

"How'd you know my name? Where am I? Why am I strapped to this table?" Patrice couldn't help the edge of hysteria creeping into her voice.

The—woman—touched Patrice's shoulder. The hand was cool and dry.

"I will answer all of your questions shortly, Patrice." She moved to the other side of the table and adjusted some knobs on the console.

Patrice strained against the restraints. "No! I want answers now, goddammit! I *demand* answers! Why am I being held here against my will? Who the hell are you?"

The being was unaffected by Patrice's tirade. In the same monotone voice, it answered, "I have been assigned to you, since it was my carelessness that brought you here. You will be studied and then released. You will not be harmed. But you must refrain from raising your voice aggressively again, or I will be forced to subdue you."

Patrice shivered. The words were calm, but the threat implied was clear.

"You went through the gateway before I could close it," the being continued. "I know your name because you carry identification. Where you are is difficult to explain. As I said, you will not be intentionally harmed. We simply wish to give you a series of tests and with the use of electronic impulses attached to your brain, we will monitor your physiological responses."

"No! I won't let you fuck with my brain! I'm not a guinea pig, goddamn it! Let me go! Let me—"

Patrice felt her body begin to warm and tingle. With a gasp, she felt her pelvic muscles begin to expand and contract. "Oh god! Oh God!!!" she yelled as a tremendous orgasm racked her body.

"Blood pressure, body temperature up, heartbeat and aspiration rate increased."

"What the hell—what are you doing to me?" Patrice panted as the spasms diminished.

"We are studying your species' sexuality. You humans are extraordinarily motivated by it."

This was too weird. Patrice dug her nails into her palms until it hurt. Yup. She was awake. She tried to recall all of the movies she had seen about UFOs and stuff like that. The heroes always got away by befriending the enemy and then outsmarting them. Okay. Okay. Let's try friendly.

"If I'm going to be kept here against my will, we may as well be properly introduced. You know my name—who are you?"

The being answered, "I am Xenobia."

"Xenobia. Okay, Xenobia. Why this fascination? Is what turns you on so different?" Patrice tried to make her voice sound suggestive. She chuckled to herself, "Do you come here often? What's your zodiac sign?" Stay focused, don't get hysterical, Patrice warned herself.

Xenobia turned to Patrice. "I do not understand this term *turn on.*"

Patrice smiled archly. "Come on—what makes you hot—gives you pleasure. What, um—what makes your heartbeat and aspiration rate increase?"

Xenobia answered, "We do not indulge in such primitive activities."

"Humph." Patrice grunted. "So in other words, you don't have sex." She mulled this over in her mind, an idea forming.

"I like to—" Xenobia turned a dial, cutting off Patrice's words as she was flooded with orgasmic sensations that seemed never ending, until Patrice screamed, tears falling from her eyes.

"Stop that! Why are you torturing me? You said you weren't going to hurt me!"

Xenobia leaned over Patrice, curiously touching the salty drops on her cheek. "I was not torturing you. I was giving you pleasure because you are cooperating."

"Endless orgasms may sound wonderful, but they're not! Orgasm after orgasm is too intense to be pleasurable."

A light bulb went off in Patrice's head. Well, she reasoned, she'd done kinkier things for less important reasons. Without missing a beat, Patrice asked, "Orgasm is not the only goal or motivator of our sexuality, Xenobia. Why don't you let me up, so I can show you what I mean."

Xenobia considered for a moment, her eyes burning orange around the edges, and then loosened the restraints holding Patrice, helping her to a sitting position. There didn't seem to be any doors in the smooth, black walls. Shit. Patrice had better satisfy, if she was going to convince Xenobia to lead her out of this nightmare.

Shaking her limbs, Patrice stood and stretched. Then she turned to Xenobia. "Why don't you take off your suit. It's much nicer touching skin to skin."

Xenobia complied, unzipping her jumpsuit neck to waist. It fell silently to the floor. Xenobia stood before Patrice, now naked.

"Thank the Goddess, she's anatomically correct." Patrice sighed to herself. She studied Xenobia's body. It was pretty androgynous—small, high breasts, the nipples an electric blue against her perfect, black skin. Her hair, head and pubic, was short and also a vivid blue. She had tiny silver markings on her arms, legs, and belly—swirls and moons and stars.

Patrice generally preferred more fleshy women, but she found Xenobia strangely erotic. "I really am out on the edge." she thought to herself as she reached out to touch the irresistible designs on Xenobia's thighs.

Xenobia stood, holding her clipboard, as Patrice trailed her fingertips over the strange grooves. Xenobia's body transmitted pleasant little electric shocks to Patrice. The currents ran through Patrice's fingertips and down to her pussy. Patrice was getting really turned on.

"What is the point of your actions, right now?" Xenobia asked as Patrice slid her hand between Xenobia's legs.

Patrice sighed irritably at the interruption, and took the clipboard, tossing it on the table. "Just pay attention. There will be a quiz immediately following. Now part your legs."

Xenobia did, and Patrice slipped her hand further into the mysterious folds. It felt human to Patrice—warm, damp. The scent though, that was different. Patrice manipulated Xenobia's slick cavern, and finding her clitoris, a small, hard kernel, Patrice stroked and flicked it. Her own pussy started to throb as she observed Xenobia's pubic hair turn a brilliant, electric blue with excitement.

Patrice slipped a finger into Xenobia, gripping and pulling her silky insides. Xenobia stood still, eyes closed, nostrils flaring, as Patrice slowly pumped her.

Patrice slipped in another finger, and then another. Each time she did so, Xenobia's hairs glowed brighter.

Patrice helped Xenobia to the floor and leaned over her, playing with the tiny blue buds on Xenobia's breasts as she twisted her hand inside Xenobia's tight orifice.

"Umph," Patrice grunted to herself, "I could fit my entire hand in here."

Working the rest of her hand, slowly, carefully up into Xenobia until her wrist brushed the flowing blue hairs, Patrice shifted her body until Xenobia's knee was positioned between her thighs, pressing hard against her throbbing pussy.

In the nocturnal light of the chamber, Xenobia's skin glowed. The silver markings on her body sparkled. Patrice closed her hand into a tight fist and began pumping Xenobia as she ground her own aching sex into Xenobia's leg.

Xenobia had forgotten Patrice, lost in the primal world of lust, long forgotten by her people. She rode Patrice's fist, rising up and slamming down as Patrice rocked her faster and faster.

Xenobia let out a high keen as her body buckled forward. Her eyes popped open, unseeing, now blood red. Xenobia clamped her muscles tightly around Patrice's fist inside her and pounded down on Patrice's slippery arm. Patrice felt Xenobia's skin heat up. The warmth spread to Patrice's body, quickening her pulse, her body tingling with the sensation.

Xenobia came, flowing like lava down Patrice's arm. Patrice fell to her knees, an orgasm swelling over her so strongly, she fainted.

When she awoke, Xenobia was standing over her, dressed again in her uniform. Patrice realized that she was also dressed in her jogging sweats.

"It is time for you to go. Please hurry, the gateway is open. We will be leaving here soon."

Patrice got up. "Back to—your home?"

Xenobia's eyes were yellow again, but flecked with bits of purple. "Yes. Now please hurry." Then she turned and walked to the wall, which slid open, revealing a dusky hallway. At the end of the corridor, Patrice could make out a hazy vision of the park. It was still early morning, by the light.

She turned to Xenobia. "So you go back to a world of dry science and no pleasure? I got the feeling you kinda liked being 'primitive.' Why don't you stay longer—we could do more research."

Xenobia's eyes pulsed. "Our studies have determined that your world is a violent, dangerous place."

Patrice took her hand. "Well, yes, it can be pretty scary, but it can also be a lot of fun—filled with exciting things to do and see and feel. You could always leave if you didn't like it. That's more than the rest of us can do."

"No. I would not be able to return home. I would become human. The gateway would be closed to me forever."

"That's rough," Patrice said quietly.

"Yes—rough." Xenobia became brisk. "Time is running out. Please. Just relax and walk through. You may experience some vertigo once you pass back into your world, but the feeling will fade. Good-bye—Patrice."

Patrice touched Xenobia's cheek. "Good-bye." Then she turned and walked into the light.

When the cold air hit her, Patrice staggered, dropping to her knees as a wave of nausea washed over her.

After a moment, she stood and looked at the bush. It wavered, not quite a mirage. Strangely, Patrice felt sad. She had kind of liked Xenobia. Ah well. An experience she would always remember and never be able to share at cocktail parties. She turned and started toward home.

At the bend of the road, she looked back. A flash of silver blinded her. When her vision cleared she saw—a figure—standing slowly, looking around. It was—yes! Xenobia! Patrice headed back toward her, and then stopped.

Xenobia had changed. Her skin had faded to a smooth, dark brown, the geometric etching on her cheek gone. Her eyes had dimmed to a soft, honey brown. She was breathtaking. Exotic. An African queen. She smiled at Patrice.

"I was hoping you might extend—how do you say—some 'down home' hospitality to a stranded sister."

Patrice laughed. "You're learning fast." She took Xenobia's hand and led her from the park.

The wall of unsaid things

Karen Green

Have you ever tried and tried to touch someone? It's interesting when they are confined and you are free. You must come to them. And even though maybe there are no chains, there are walls. Perhaps it seems they must be scalable, but you are only on the outside of them. How can you know how big they look from the inside? How can you tell through the brick and the blood her height, her ability, her intention?

I cruised up to the sidewalk on my little Honda. I saw Mercury standing in the yard. The noise of the bike drew her to the fence immediately.

"Nice bike," she said, smiling.

"Yeah. Want a ride?" I asked, returning the smile.

"Can't. I'm sort of busy, you know." She motioned with her head towards the factory building behind her.

"Let me guess. You get off at five?" I joked.

"Well, actually. I never get off." Her smirk was revealing. I had to admit I was charmed. We laughed under our breaths.

"Come back at ten, over by that gate to the south," she whispered.

I smiled. "What's your name?"

"Mercury," she replied.

"Ah, so you're an elemental, so to speak?" I asked.

"Think what you want," she said, unmoved.

I walked towards the front gate. She followed me momentarily, but a whistle went off and she instinctively returned to the factory.

I entered the gate of the detention center, where two female guards waved me past. They undoubtedly remembered me from last summer.

I used to stop by the prison a lot. I went inside the building to the warden's outer office.

"Well, Doctor," said the warden's assistant, "I am sure we'll be able to help you. I take it you received the list of potential workers that might be useful to you."

My experiments had been lacking in a certain feminine quality. I had told the women's detention center that I'd gladly take a candidate for rehabilitation and put them to work in the name of science. This was a common arrangement between the labs and the detention center. No one really thought twice about it.

"Well, yes," I replied. "I went over the notes you gave me. I would like to interview Ms. Mercury Webber. I hope we can do this now, as I really do have urgent matters in the lab that need my attention."

"Oh, certainly, Doctor. I'll have Ms. Webber brought in immediately," said the assistant. She picked up the phone and dialed.

"Sergeant, please bring number two thousand twenty-three up to the warden's office," she ordered.

Within seconds, I was face to face with the woman I'd just seen in the yard.

"Mercury, this is a doctor to interview you about working in the laboratory," the assistant explained. She then turned to me. "Ms. Webber has been very eager to be of some service outside the factory. She's an intelligent woman."

"Yes, I see. Ms. Webber, you attended college for several years," I said.

Mercury stood with her head bowed and her hands clasped together. There was something subtle, something about her position that unsettled me. I couldn't shake the feeling that maybe I had made a mistake.

"Is there something wrong, Ms. Webber?" I asked. "You look, uh, disappointed."

"I wasn't very good at science, Doctor," she said. Her eyes would not meet mine.

"It's not a requirement that you know anything about science, Ms. Webber. The position is clerical, primarily, and anything that interests you to learn," I replied.

"Mercury, don't offend the doctor," barked the assistant.

Mercury pressed her upper front teeth into her lower lip.

"I'd like you to have Ms. Webber's things collected," I said. "She will do quite well with us, I'm sure. I'll be waiting in Warden Metzger's office. She asked me to stop by. Thank you."

"So, you chose Mercury, Doctor," said the warden, looking up at me and smiling. "She's an odd one.

"Do you want my honest opinion?" she asked.

"Are you jealous, Francis? Tired of this place yet?" I remarked.

"Doctor, just because you and I have a past doesn't mean we have a future," she said. No doubt she was very right.

There was a knock on the door.

"Watch out, Doctor. She'll run," Francis whispered, and then sternly she said, "Come in."

Mercury entered wearing jeans and a Yankees sweatshirt. She still stood with her head lowered, staring at the floor.

"Well, thank you, Doctor," the warden finished, returning her eyes to her desk and writing something down. She paused and looked up, "And if there are any difficulties, you will let me know?"

"Thank you, Warden," I said. "I'll call you next week and update you."

We shook hands and walked out of the office towards the front door. Mercury and I said nothing as we passed out of the gates of the prison and over to my Honda.

"I guess you're getting off a little earlier today," I said.

Mercury's face remained still. Silently, she put on the helmet I gave her. At my command, she swung her leg over the back of the bike. She held on behind the seat. I had a feeling she wouldn't be putting her arms around me. I was surprised to find that I actually cared.

That night, while I tried to help Mercury settle in, Dr. O. came by. She had been in her lab for hours running tests on a certain hermaphroditic fetal tissue. I knew her visit was only partially to hand over the samples, but I kept silent about it.

"So, did you get any results yet?" I asked.

"No, maybe you can do something with these samples tonight," she said. "Do you have time."

This wasn't a question. Dr. O. was my primary supervisor. There was no denying her various requests. Dr. O. began to scour my laboratory. She ran her hands along the benches, then sniffed her finger tips. This particular ritual I always found fiendishly irritating.

"What?" I asked.

"Never you mind what I do. I want you to call when you finish," she ordered.

Dr. O. sauntered out and slammed the door.

I put the samples aside in the lab. I was worried. Usually I would run tests immediately. I knew if I didn't get back to her within an hour, she'd be back.

The island had been so hot lately. Steaming and thick and unbearable. It made my already insane lust impossibly irritating. My lab was becoming a stifling cell where my fantasies were taking more time than the experiments.

My new house guest wasn't helping. I knew it would be wrong to engage her; there were plenty of women who would willingly satisfy me. But I couldn't stop thinking about how much I wanted Mercury in my room.

I knew that Dr. O. would consider her a distraction. But I was beginning to think that true concentration could only occur during periods of supreme obsession. Work then would become the only release of the sublimated energy. Dr. O. would have agreed, but she was the sort of girl who couldn't admit it.

This experiment started out as a letter. Out of the blue, or actually out of red. And this actually started long ago. Inside. That is where the stream begins. There sits beside the water a row of houses and there are ships docked nearby.

In the letter I told her that what I was trying to do was overcome a certain historic dynamic. I had just started to write a paper about the connections I had made between flying saucers (based on Jung's analysis) and ostracism. I called it Our Alien Visitors: Projection or Protection. *This paper was inspirational; while writing, it occurred to me that had I a compliant assistant, I could take the experiments to completion.*

The letter described to her my current location. It had the distinct impression of a map. Really, the problem was she didn't remember the way.

I conceded to Dr. O., yes, I wanted to fuck all the time. It could have been the heat or being cooped up in the lab, or even the food. I felt different when I first came to the island. Five years ago, I was twenty-three, coming out of an intense medical research program in Austin, Texas. When the government recruited me for their finest team on cell deterioration, I was honored and excited about the many resources becoming available. I had planned to marry that year, but my commitment to science was frightening to the woman who had known me since my nerd days in high school.

So, when the government asked me to go to a secret lab on an uncharted island, I saw the opportunity to be free of romantic entanglements. What I wasn't told was that a nearby detention center for women provided many scientists with secretaries, technicians, and other labor resources.

So that Dr. O. would stop being jealous, I assured her my obsession was of a scientific nature.

"What's her name?" she asked.

"Mercury," I said.

"What did she do, you know, to get put in the prison?"

"I don't know. She used to be a stand-up magician—saws people in half, you know, that type of shtick," I replied, trying to sound disinterested.

Being a scientist, however, Mercury's profession turned me on.

Three years ago I met Dr. O. She sat at the other end of the bar. She ordered a tequila shot. I am not a vodka, gin and tonic, or rum drinker by any means. You may occasionally catch me basking in nostalgia with some sort of whiskey, what was available in my parents' liquor cabinet. Only a certain type of spirit, though, can take in the tequila-shot poison and incorporate it without squeamishness. That's definitely the sexiest move any girl can make at a bar.

I walked over to her, impressed. She looked familiar; I didn't realize she was famous. Didn't play the typical cards.

You know, you walk up behind the girl, ordering a drink while a hand rubs up against her ass, she looks at you. You stare deeply. Start talking, understand all the things she says. Say what she wants to hear.

She begins to think it's cosmic. It's love at first sight. You go home with her and fuck her brains out. She's never really come like that before with anyone so she's excited and becomes hooked. You hold her all night, get her phone number. Never call, and then your answering machine has daily messages. And though you are sympathetic, you know you really shouldn't pull her in. She couldn't handle the reality behind it.

Dr. O. was different from the beginning. She begged for a chase, but when she ran she made any catch impossible. So you could kiss her hello, and you could begin with your tongue spreading apart her lips. But you could not touch.

The first day I had believed Mercury was easy. She was just a rugged substance, something that needed love and attention. Mercury was just the sort of girl that attracted walls.

I had felt a sincere sympathy on seeing her in the yard that day. Like we had been sixteen together. Giddy, daring. She would hold my ass as we walked down the hall in school. Make out for the precious afternoon hours before parents intervened.

But then, in the office I understood I wouldn't be seeing her like that soon. But then, I denied the possibility that I wouldn't ever see her like that again.

The first night was simple. I got to watch her jerk off. Her door was ajar when I went to make sure she was asleep. I knew this was a bit of a gift. But it was a torturous one. I watched for a moment and went to my room. We deserved this one night off. I left her to drift throughout her body alone.

The next morning led me to the decision that Mercury posed difficulties. I began to acknowledge my personal intentions. But I felt implicitly that she had some cosmic significance.

From the long look on her face and the strange taste of her scrambled eggs, I gathered she was unhappy with the arrangement.

"Mercury, I thought you cooked in the prison. You can't make a simple egg?"

I didn't believe the warden. I knew Mercury wouldn't run. Where would she go? But then, I had locked the door to her room, just in case. I would be held responsible. I had the law to justify locking the door. That didn't comfort me.

Name: Mercury Webber
Occupation: Clerical
Residence: Lab 405

I gave the ID card a glance for accuracy and then handed it to Mercury.

"Mercury, you're required to keep this with you at all times. If you want to leave the house, you just slide the card through this slot and the door will open. Do you have a safe place for it?"

"Yes, Master," she replied.

"What's that supposed to mean?" I asked hotly.

"Relax," she said. "You're just treating me like I'm some ditzy girl with no brain. I didn't get to these lovely accommodations on looks alone."

She shot me a knowing look and finished. "You know you can be incredibly condescending. You should really learn how to deal with women with a little more respect. Who knows where it might get you."

She smiled and went upstairs saying, "I'm taking a shower. I'll clean the kitchen later."

I huffed. Mercury had only been here two days and I felt like I had a wife already. I figure, that's how these girls wear you down. They push at you and push at you and you get to this point where all you want to do is keep them from getting upset. I don't think a day went by with my fiancée that I didn't apologize for being inattentive. I got so tired of trying to give that a big wall grew there and I needed to leave. She just thought it was about fucking and how she wouldn't let me fuck her the way I really liked. But that wasn't really it. I think eventually she would have let me do whatever I wanted, but I couldn't bring myself to do it. She was so young and I had already taken so much of her innocence. Her insecurities about us made her so needy for attention, she turned me off. On top of that, I was dying for some experiences.

Mercury is a different creature altogether. Mercury reminds me that she is watery yet like the wind. She skirts along the silvery border with a slight scent and avid potential for transformation. Mercury was designed from the firmest genetic substance. Her ability to withstand pain and pressure is impressive.

I looked at the kitchen from the stairwell. Just past the waist-high counter I could see the leftovers from our meal sitting near the sink. I didn't like the lab to get too messy because of the germs, and Mercury was fairly respectful of that. I was under the impression, though, that housecleaning wasn't her favorite task. The research labs were set up in concentric circles around the Main Labs in the center. Each researcher had at least one private lab area in her apartment, and the apartments were standard government housing. You didn't have so much say about the space. Your level and your work pretty much determined your place.

I had above-average accommodations. Dr. O. had seen to it that I had a lab where I could do all the work I needed for our experiments, and a smaller lab for my own personal pet project. Dr. O. must have done a little bargaining for it, though, because we never had to submit a report on the reason we wanted a spare room. She said she told them it was a backup because sometimes our timing was so crucial, we couldn't make it to the Main Labs.

The "home" part of the apartment consisted of three bedrooms, two bathrooms and a small phone room on the top floor. On the second floor was my big lab and there was a special door to get to it. The ground floor had three medium-sized rooms and the kitchen. The kitchen was at the back of the apartment, and there were sliding glass doors that went out onto a small patch of grass. Although my apartment was fortunate enough to have an avocado tree, eating the avocados somehow wasn't appetizing.

That evening, Dr. O. had come by and asked about my "new house guest."

"She's a clerical worker," I said. "I can't do the bullshit work anymore, you know that. I'm too busy as it is."

Dr. O. smiled and approached me. She rubbed the palm of her hand against my cheek. She whispered, "You are so simple, Doctor. You believe your own lies, that's the magic you are working."

My instinct was to pull away, but I didn't. I didn't want to give in, to express the weakness I felt. Instead I smiled, leaned in, and ran my lips across hers. I sensed her mouth part and pushed my tongue to spread her lips. She responded with her tongue, momentarily. My hand rubbed against her erect nipple, but when I took my lips away from her mouth to look at her breast, she pulled back a bit.

"You're such a good kisser," she said.

"Take off your clothes," I commanded.

She smiled, acquiescing. She stood up in front of the kitchen counter and let her blouse fall to the floor. She turned around and pushed her jeans down over her ass. I got up, bent her back slightly forward, so she was leaning over the counter.

"Haven't you always wondered," I whispered into her ear, "what it would be like to have my fingers in your pussy?"

She looked back at me. "I want you to fuck me with your cock."

I hesitated, and rubbed my hand in between her thighs and along her pussy.

She pushed her ass back against my groin. I was reaching for my zipper when I heard a noise upstairs.

"Shit," said Dr. O., and pulled her clothes back on. "I didn't know you let her loose in the house. Jesus, you better be careful. If she saw that, then what do you think might happen?"

"Dr. O.," I said, "don't worry about it. She senses the tension between us."

"I don't know what you think you're up to but you better get your priorities straight," said Dr. O. She started towards the door, but I grabbed her.

I told her, "Listen, honey, you're right. I should have been more careful. But don't rush out, that will look bad, too. Sit and talk to me for a bit and then we'll get you home."

During our conversation, Dr. O. told me I was making everything difficult. She said if I just sat down and focused, all the things would fall slowly into place. No doubt she was correct, but my mind had its own need for diversion.

Dr. O. asked me to spell out in specific detail the lust that was driving me away from work.

"Dr. O.," I began, "you are my true love, as if you are a portion of myself that has become you and is not really me anymore. But is that a reason to abandon me? And my desires. I desire you, but while you are so irritable, I can only look for something to contain me. It's part of the process."

Dr. O. knew I would be a good lay. But she had resisted for so long. I was glad she was starting to give in. It could, however, change the focus of the work. Or so I thought.

I called Dr. O. the next day; she didn't return the call. I'd heard from a student in one of her classes that she'd gone on a week of vacation. My retaliation was weak but necessary. I went to Mercury towards the end of the week and invited her to begin working in the lab. She wasn't thrilled at the prospect, but she agreed.

"Look," I said, "It's gotta be a little more interesting than doing the dishes, right?"

steam

Jeannine DeLombard

Flashing her ID to the Lycra-molded, thong-wearing blond gym bunny as she walked into the Y, Jordan was reminded of her conversation with the guys at Kelly's Tavern the night before. Straight, they simply could not understand how she, a dyke, could go to the Y everyday and not be overwhelmed by the bouncing breasts, perky butts and tight calves that were always on display in the locker room. Entering it now, about an hour later than usual—she had stopped at the gas company to see what would be involved in converting to gas heat, knowing those old radiators wouldn't last forever—she noticed that the locker room was almost empty. Too bad, she could have used the distraction of people-watching. Not girl-watching, she thought, throwing down her gym bag and impatiently twisting the knob on her combination lock. Remembering how she had responded to Bob and Al's jocular amazement with her characteristic gruffness—informing them coolly that she could eat pussy and work out with it too, that being surrounded by the very objects of her desire didn't faze her as it would them—she wondered why she answered them the way she did, why she didn't just tell them the truth.

But what exactly was the truth, Jordan wondered as she started to undress, gazing down at high, firm breasts dotted with the occasional mole and framed by her deeply tanned, hard upper arms. For the truth was that no one at the gym—in or out of the locker room—interested her. Like the woman who checked her ID, they all seemed to be aerobicized, Nautilized versions of the same type—lean, pristine, and made-to-order. She knew if she told her drinking buddies that, they'd not only shake their heads in disbelief, but think her even stranger than they already did. Her job on the road crew of the Pennsylvania Department of Transportation gave her one-of-the-boys status in the bar. But just as the guys on the job always reminded her that she was a woman by making sure that she got stuck with the least challenging and most dangerous task—flagger—they reminded her too that she was a dyke with their never-ending questions and uneasy ribbing. If she told them she simply wasn't attracted to the babes that lubricated their fantasies, they wouldn't believe her—they'd just bust her chops and talk about sour grapes.

Worst of all, Jordan reflected as she sauntered topless over to the toilets, past a bulky figure almost hidden by the mists in the gang shower, she was afraid that they were right. Outward appearances, she knew, confirmed that she was a dyke: her gravelly, mumbling way of talking; her long, confident stride; her jeans and workshirts; hell, even her job on the PennDOT road crew screamed dyke—that was easy for anyone to see. What was harder to perceive were her inner doubts and anxieties. The few times she had ventured into the women's bar in Philly she had taken a woman home, almost as if to prove something to herself. Every time it was the same. At first the very prospect of being with these women excited her: the breasts spilling out as she unhooked their lacy bras, the round ass emerging as she carefully removed their pantyhose. Yet, when faced with their nude, expectant bodies, she lost all interest. Was it sour grapes? Were the women in bars like that somehow inferior to those who gave themselves to men, to her drinking buddies? Or was she just a sexual freak—attracted to neither men nor women? What made these women so uninspiring for her?

Thinking about this—something she usually tried not to do—upset her, and she slammed the stall door, making the woman in front of the mirror interrupt her pre-stepclass makeup session to look up sharply at Jordan. Feeling awkward and out of place, Jordan thought about calling today a wash and just going home. She didn't think she was up to the nonverbal competition that always took place between her and the guys in the weight room. Not today. Today she wanted to let off some steam, but not in the usual ways, by lifting or drinking. She wanted a different kind of release. Instead of heading back to her locker, Jordan went to a part of the locker room she seldom visited, where the sauna and steam room were. Entering the latter, her jeans still on, Jordan thought wryly to herself, if this doesn't do it, nothing will.

At first the billows of white air and the hissing pipes made her panic, blocking her lungs and nose. But soon the dim fog calmed her and she sat down on one of the concrete benches that lined the small, tiled room. Shutting her eyes, she imagined her tension dissipating into the vapor that surrounded her. Work, the guys at Kelly's, the indifferent parade of nude women—none of that seemed to matter any more. Jordan felt her pores, her lungs, her very soul being purified by the hot whiteness. After a while, when the hissing had stopped and the air cleared a bit, Jordan became aware of the itchy dampness of her jeans and decided to take a cold shower. Hell, maybe she'd even lift after all. When she opened her eyes, however, she was startled to see standing in front of her the woman she had noticed showering earlier. Trying not to be rude, she couldn't help but stare at the woman's sumptuous breasts spilling over her ample belly, which jutted out defiantly, almost obscuring her wide, lush hips and her abundant thighs. Breaking out of her trance, Jordan felt instantly embarrassed and opened her mouth. Before she could say anything, however, the woman cupped her heavy breasts in her arms and mashed Jordan's face into them.

At first Jordan, feeling ridiculous and ashamed, tried to pull away. But the woman was stronger than she looked, and her breasts were both reassuring and exciting. Slowly, aware that she had just lost a battle of some sort, Jordan stretched her arms around the woman's plush waist in a futile attempt to contain her and, thereby, to regain control. But she couldn't. Instead, she stood, pushing the woman down as she did so, registering with satisfaction the gentle smack of the woman's flesh as it made contact with the hard tile floor. Realizing how hot the woman's skin felt against her own steaming skin, it occurred to Jordan what she was about to do.

Kneeling, she reached down to put her hands between the woman's legs. As she tried to spread the woman's thighs, Jordan's rough, callused hands quickly got lost in the soft, pressing, resistant flesh. She was surprised; somehow she had assumed they would respond to her touch just as a sealed envelope slides effortlessly open when held over boiling water. Glimpsing the curly light-brown hair that was all but covered by the two voluminous thighs, Jordan was inspired to renew her efforts. Realizing that pushing harder would only create more resistance, she decided to knead the flesh as she would dough in an attempt to make its plump firmness yield to her desires. She was rewarded to feel the woman's body relax and the legs finally separate. Rewarded and frustrated anew, for as they did, the woman's abundant belly cascaded down between them like lava, once again filling the crevice she had struggled so hard to expose.

Frustration gave way to admiration—awe, really—as Jordan gazed upon the seemingly endless expanse of soft white skin in front of her, an expanse punctuated only by the pucker that she supposed marked the woman's navel. Somewhere in the recesses of her mind she marveled that this massive being had once been contained in a space as small or smaller than the one to which she was so determined to gain entry.

The woman was quiet. Not a moan or a sigh to tell Jordan to go ahead, to touch here, caress there. For a second, Jordan was tempted to give up. Fucking bitch, she should be happy to get it this good. Then she stopped herself, suddenly aware that the privilege and the pleasure were all hers, aware that the woman, by letting Jordan immerse herself in her boundless softness, was doing *her* the favor— a favor that Jordan was anxious to repay.

As she realized this, Jordan noticed that the slight jiggle in the flesh of the woman's stomach was increasing rapidly, that it echoed the sudden heaving in her chest, a heaving that made her huge flattened breasts bob and toss about like waves on a stormy sea. Clearly the woman wanted to be fucked almost as badly as Jordan wanted to fuck her. Perhaps, Jordan speculated, eyeing once again the seemingly impenetrable folds of flesh that blocked entrance to the woman's pussy, perhaps she is as frustrated as I am. Perhaps she wished she was as flat and skinny as a supermodel, and that I could reach down and finger her just like that. Thanking God that she couldn't, Jordan plunged her hands into the deep horizontal line that separated the woman's stomach from the tops of her thighs.

Pushing the woman so that she lay all the way down on the floor, its hard whiteness contrasting with the flushed softness of her skin, Jordan pressed her own body flat against the damp tiles, and was delighted to find herself inches away from the woman's open, moist pussy. Of course it was big, soft and inviting like the rest of her. But still, Jordan hadn't expected this and was amazed by the pussy's plump fleshiness as she sunk her tongue onto the woman's swollen clit.

She had only been there a few seconds when she realized that she was being enveloped by the woman's body, her huge thighs pressing against Jordan's face and neck, the firm belly bearing down from above. Distracted only momentarily by a feeling of claustrophobia, Jordan regretted putting the woman on her back. She wanted to continue to fight that stubborn flesh, as she had to get where she was now. Deftly, she maneuvered herself onto her back, pulling the woman over her as she did so. Now the woman was sitting on Jordan's face, her round knees anchored firmly on either side of Jordan's face. Her voluptuous thighs cushioned Jordan's head, rendering the tile floor benign. Resuming her ministrations, Jordan tried to see beyond the underbelly that jiggled in time to her increasingly frenzied tongue strokes. Hoping to catch a glimpse of the woman's face, and there to read her desire and excitement, Jordan realized the futility of her effort and resigned herself to reaching up and, grabbing the woman by her gently pumping hips, pulling her warm fullness even closer into her face. Suddenly aware of the throbbing in her own clit, Jordan thought of reaching down to touch herself. Before she could, however, she felt her hips rise into the air, and her pussy contracting repeatedly with the waves that washed over her. All she could do was press her face even more deeply into the woman's pussy, rolling the hard, tart sweetness of her clit on her tongue the way you would a raspberry in a mouthful of champagne.

In her post-orgasmic stupor, Jordan observed that the woman, while excited, was nowhere near climax. Briefly, Jordan was tempted to succumb to her own satiety and exhaustion, to shove the woman away, leaving her breathless and wanting on the tile floor as she walked out of the steam room and got dressed. No lovely reciprocity, no awkward attempts at politeness—how liberating that would be.

The only thing that held her there was the insistent warmth that slowly flooded the area between her legs. At first she tried to ignore it, but, as it grew more persistent, she tried to devise ways to appease it. Gripping the woman's hips even more firmly, she wrestled them, still thrusting, down again to the floor. Standing, she looked at the woman through the lingering dampness. The woman's eyes were shut; her face, turned to one side, impassive but for the faintly creased forehead, the slightly flared nostrils and the dry lips, which she sought to moisten with the pink tip of her tongue. Her body, which shocked Jordan all over again with its pliant immensity, rocked slightly, its creases and rolls reconfiguring themselves with each new movement. As Jordan eased off her worn, damp Levi's, revealing bicycle shorts, and, beneath them a pair of thinly jutting hips and another, lower bulge, Jordan knew that she would not leave—could not—until she had fucked this woman as God, nature, or the planets had clearly intended her to be fucked.

Crouching as she peeled off the Lycra shorts, Jordan lowered herself onto the soft, billowing bed that was the woman's body, and slipped herself—or, rather, that part of her which was not herself—into the woman's wet, waiting pussy. Bracing herself against first the floor, then the warm, full rolls on the sides of the woman's body, Jordan slammed into her with a force bordering on fury. Looking down, she dimly saw the woman's breasts as they jerked and swelled in time to her rhythmic thrusts. Gazing at the abundant belly that helped to hold them in check, Jordan was just beginning to marvel anew at the abandon with which it spilled across her hips when she felt a tremor deep in the woman's body. Like the sensation you get when you touch the railroad tracks and feel the rumble of a distant train, Jordan felt both curiosity and terror, anxious to see the promise fulfilled and yet afraid that its coming would destroy her by its sheer force. As the tremor turned into a pounding and the pounding turned into an explosion, Jordan held onto the woman's churning, thrashing body, pumping her own hips until she too exploded.

As they lay there, spent and gasping for air, the faint hissing sound resumed, and Jordan felt her sweaty body grow increasingly damp as steam once again filled the room. She eased out of the woman, pulling herself up and, with a twinge of regret, off those gently pressing breasts and the firm convexity of that stomach. Groping, her eyes still shut, Jordan made her way over to the bench, which was somehow reassuring in its hardness. She sat there for a while, not thinking, not moving. Opening her eyes, she felt herself in a dream, surrounded by the clouds of hot, white air. Focusing, her eyes sought the form of the body that had given her such amazing pleasure, only to be distracted by the shaft of light and cool air that shot through the suddenly opened door—a light that was immediately obscured by the shadow of the figure who stepped into it, ushered out by billows of steam.

Baila conmigo

Lauren Voloshen

I sat down on my bed and looked at George sleeping in the other one. He was a good photographer but not someone I could be intimate with. Sharing the last available hotel room with him wasn't comfortable. He stank and he slept noisily. Although the lights were out and the curtain was drawn, light from the courtyard seeped in bright enough for me to make out muted colors. Between those lights, George's snoring, the party noise, my recent adrenaline rush, and the thermos of coffee I had drunk on the ride up, I knew I couldn't sleep. I went back to the bathroom and rinsed off my face and brushed my teeth. I considered taking a bath. The tub was deluxe, even if it was a little shabby with yellow stains and chipped enamel. It was long and deep.

But I had too much energy to sit in hot water. I felt more like swimming or lifting weights or dancing. I was jittery. Drinking crossed my mind, but I hadn't brought anything with me, and on second thought, I figured alcohol would only prolong my problem. I resigned myself to a sleepless night and headed to the diner with a couple of newspapers that I found on the dresser.

Another woman was there when I arrived, another *extranjera,* and no one else. When I looked at her I had an eerie sensation, a feeling that she and I were meant to meet. I dismissed it as fantasy. She sat in the first booth, right up against the front door.

I knew right away that she was a dyke. She had short, light brown hair, a square jaw and square shoulders. Her eyes were other-worldly and worked a hypnotic power on me the second I met them. Her mouth was full and tinted so deeply, so wetly, that her lips appeared to be stained rather than glossed maroon, provocative maroon, thick and glistening like plum sauce, like burgundy, like blood. But no makeup had been applied to her eyes. They were enormous and golden. Taunting eyes from a dream. They owned her face and commanded all of her other features.

I stared at her.

I was hung over and buzzing with insomnia. Alone I would have drifted in self-examination. I would have run smack up against my fears. And then I would have crumbled. I itched for anything, and there in front of me was an enigmatic woman with blond eyes and fat, red lips.

A straight woman would never have the self-confidence to look back at me in the way that this woman looked back.

She wore mismatched earrings and a powder-blue *guayabera,* barely buttoned over her breasts. One earring was a small glass globe with something I couldn't make out floating in the center of it and the other was a tiny seahorse. She held my gaze to the brink of discomfort, then grinned slightly and gave me a nod.

I hadn't seen another lesbian in months. Looking at her gave me a rush of excitement and comfort. I felt like I had just finished a long swim. I looked over the counter to the clerk and asked him for a cup of coffee, and the lesbian said, *"Bueno. Aquí tienen nada mas."* Her accent was blatantly formal. Castillian, but not quite. I figured she was European.

"Hablas inglés?" I said in deliberate slang.

"Most likely better than you," she answered quite Britishly and with a knee-weakening impish grin.

And I said, "Can I join you?"

"You may," she answered. I got my coffee and slid into her booth. I could see into the globe earring. The floating thing in the center had once been alive. I wasn't sure what it was though. I thought it might be some kind of a slug since slugs, like seahorses, are androgynous. It would have been a cynical commentary on the lesbian use of seahorses to signal our sexuality, and I found the idea humorous. I leaned over the table to study it.

"It's a tequila worm," the lesbian said. "I made it myself. I could make one for you, if you'd like."

"No, look," I said. I put my thumbs behind my ears and pushed my lobes forward. "No holes. I don't wear jewelry."

"A little butch, are you? With all that long hair?"

My hair, tied in a ponytail, was swung forward on my shoulder.

"Well," she went on, "I hope you're not stone." Then she winked and I felt myself blush. I was as embarrassed and dumbstruck as I had ever been as a teenager. I didn't know why I felt that way, but I loved it. I wanted more of her treatment. There was something thrillingly surreal about meeting a dyke from England in the ruins of an elite resort hotel from Somoza's Nicaragua during a marathon search for a secret war. She stared at me, raised her coffee mug to her face, and kept staring. With the cup over her mouth and nose, I had only her eyes to read, and they were like independent, sentient beings perched at the edge of a cave and studying me.

My blush faded, and determination rose in its place. A woman sat across from me, unabashedly flirting with me, and I wanted her. I deserved her. I wanted my lips on her round breasts and my hands inside of her. I wanted to swirl my tongue in her ears and navel and down her belly and between her labia. I wanted to kiss and grasp and suck and scratch. My breasts swelled and my thighs clutched and I thought I was desperate and should be careful. Then I thought I was desperate and to hell with caution. Nothing kills desire like caution.

I played.

"I'm not stone," I said, grateful that my voice didn't shake, "but I like a long, slow buildup, and I can take it. But why you should ask, well, I don't even know your name."

She put down her cup and thrust her hand at me.

"Lynn." She smiled.

I shook hands with her and told her my name.

A waft of hyacinth filled my nose. The same scent that Helen wore.

Helen the beautiful, the sexy, the dangerous, who had finally dumped me homeless and lonely on the dock at the Olympia marina.

The anger resurrected with that memory of rejection, pumped up my blood pressure and magnified my instant desire for Lynn.

"Who do you work for?" she asked.

"I'm stringing for Monitor."

"The Christian Scientists? You're not one of them, are you?"

"No," I laughed. "But they pay me. How about you?"

"Well, I'm not actually a reporter or anything. I mean, I'm a student. The university arranged a press pass for me so I could get around. I'm doing a study on feminism, or I should say women's politics in Nicaragua, for my doctorate. I was over at the press office, looking for a lift up to Esteli really, when this bombing broke, and one of the fellows offered to bring me along. Thought it might be fun so I came. Tomorrow I'll be closer to Esteli."

I leaned into the corner of my bench and put my feet up. Holding my coffee cup in two hands, I tipped it to my mouth and sipped. I looked at Lynn over the rim of the cup. She looked back at me, perfectly steady. I knew that she knew that I wanted her and that I was judging her. She didn't flinch. She wasn't nervous. She smiled. The corners of her eyes crinkled, and the topaz irises glittered, and she looked straight back at me and waited.

Lynn seemed to be the woman who owned the world. At the moment, war was the backdrop in her romantic fantasy. In mine, too, even if I thought it should be something else.

I laughed and so did Lynn. I laughed so hard I had to put my cup down on the table. I thought about laughing with Luminara. I saw her in front of me, washing the dishes, not looking at me. I pushed the memory away because it drained my arousal into a morose, queasy guilt, something I did not want to examine or feel.

I leaned forward and inhaled Lynn's hyacinth deeply.

"I haven't laid eyes on anybody like you since I got to Nicaragua," I said.

"From the island you mean?" she said. She stirred her drink slowly.

"Yes. The island." I smiled.

"Well, yes, I have that problem myself. I heard about a club in Managua, but when I went by, it was filled with men."

"Just like the States," I said.

"I just remind myself that I didn't come here to date. It's just that I did expect to meet somebody."

We were silent for a bit. We sipped our drinks and looked at each other. After a few minutes, Lynn took a deep breath and spoke.

"I guess there are some of us out on the construction brigades. Especially the ones from the States."

"Yeah, well, I can't mess around with those people. It makes my editors think I'm not objective. That I've come here on some solidarity mission instead of to tell the news. Sometimes I think they believe the embassy line is the news. Anyway, it makes things tough on me all around." I plucked my cigarettes from my pocket and started to tap one out of the pack.

Lynn held up her hand and shook her head.

"Please don't," she said. "I used to have the habit, but since I quit the smell seems to make me nauseous."

"It must be hard for you in this country. Everybody smokes. They smoke on the busses." I held the pack with one cigarette dangling from the opening in front of me and tried to decide what to do.

"Yes," Lynn said, "It is rough. So do you mind? If I can control it, I like to take a little break."

"Alright," I said, and I put the smokes away.

We shared another small silence, then Lynn spoke again.

"You seem pleased with what's in front of you now," she said. Her tone was cheerfully abrupt. "So am I. Finished up there?" She pointed at my coffee with her elbow.

"It's awful," I answered.

"Think you're going to bed now?"

"I don't know. I'm kind of wired. That party is pretty noisy. I thought maybe a swim. There's a pool, right? That's it in the middle of the courtyard, right?"

"Forget it. It's half full of stale green water. The algae is already stringy, it's been growing so long. I checked it this afternoon. Come on. Come with me. I've got some instant in my room and a couple of tea bags, too. I brought my little camp stove with me and some good bottled water. Why don't you let me fix you up a cup?" She winked at me, again. "After, we can split a bottle of wine. I found some French red in Honduras for a very good price."

"Why did you come over here?" I asked. "With all that stuff in your room?"

"I thought I might meet someone, and look, I have. Now that's taken care of, why should I stick around?"

So I went with her.

In her room, just a couple doors away from where George slept, there was one double bed instead of the two singles that George and I had. Lynn hung a sleeping bag over the door and a blanket over the window, under the curtains, and managed to block out nearly all the sound from the party. Then she puttered around with her stove and the coffee. With her back to me, she asked if I wanted a bath.

"Do I stink?"

"I thought you might enjoy it. I saw you pull up. You've just had a long ride from Managua, am I right? How often do you get a bath?"

A weak but steady stream of air conditioning rumbled out of a unit under the window, but even outside the air was ten degrees cooler than in Managua. In Lynn's room a bath seemed like a better idea than it had in the room with George. While I was thinking Lynn went into the bathroom and ran the water.

She came back and smiled at me.

"Go ahead. I'll bring you your beverage."

I went. The water ran hard and steamy, if a little on the yellow side, and the tub was full by the time I undressed. It was another tub with feet, more than three-feet deep, and long enough for two. Freestanding, it was angled toward the center of the room. The tarnished brass plumbing, even a tall pipe with a broad shower head, sprouted from the floor. A canopy, which held up the shower curtain, rolled like a bamboo window blind, hung from the ceiling. I shut the faucet, clipped my hair to the top of my head and melted into the water, sighing and moaning with the pleasure, too exhausted to be self-conscious or inhibited.

The bathroom was large. The floor and the walls, to shoulder level, were covered with pale blue, square inch, ceramic tiles. Some were cracked or chipped, a couple were loose, and mildew stains outlined the ones in the corners and around the tub and toilet and bidet, but the elegance remained. Where the tiles ended on the walls, there was a row of white ones with dark blue flowers, hand painted, each one unique, under a row of three-square-inch violet tiles. The wall above boasted pastel washes and delicate, ghostly, floral murals. Gas lamps, evidently long dead, with cracked, dusty, and chipped chimneys, two on each side of the bathroom, were mounted in the middle of the murals. It all seemed very Blanche Dubois and perfect for my mood.

I leaned my head against the edge of the tub and looked down at my body. Small as it was, it seemed even smaller and more vulnerable under the water, and I laughed out loud at myself for having the audacity to live in that small, curvy, feminine body as if I were a man, tall and broad, and in command. My breasts, large and droopy, which usually hung loose on my ribs, floated above my chest. The nipples stood up like volcanoes poking out of the water. A warm, first-glass-of-wine excitement grew in my groin, spread down the inside of my thighs and up my rib cage and neck, into my head where it made me giddy. With the help of the hot water, the exhaustion beat the tension out of my muscles. My ears rang.

Lynn walked in with the coffee. She was dressed in a silk kimono. She stood beside the tub and held the cup out to me.

"It's still rather hot. Shall I put it on the floor here?"

I said yes and she set it beside the tub. When she bent over the kimono slipped and I could see her nakedness. The skin over her chest had the smooth, soft grain of a fine-milled, heavy-lather, luxury soap. When she stood up she adjusted the kimono and sat down on the closed toilet. Neither of us commented on her unannounced entrance. I watched her eyes scan my body. Her face remained passive. Then she looked at my face.

"Is that your boyfriend who drove you? You're not married. You don't have a ring," she said.

"He's a photographer. We have a professional relationship. It's my car. He drove because I was too tired."

Lynn laughed.

"And you can't keep your eyes open now, can you?"

I laughed.

"Mind if I get in there with you?" Lynn said, and I kept laughing, and she stood up and let her kimono slide, hesitating at her elbows, then at her hips, then off her solid, husky body.

She stepped in and the water surged around my shoulders. For a moment she straddled me. She leaned forward for a second. The fuzzy, copper hairs over her mons tickled my nose. She smelled like the ocean, as fresh and dank. My mouth watered. Her round and taut belly came to my face. Then her breasts. She slid under the water, between my legs and into my vagina in one steamy, sinewy move. She faded in and out of focus through the steam. Her hyacinth mixed with sweat and mildew in the steam, and the smell intoxicated me. I held onto the sides of the tub and waited for a peak in my excitement. I had never felt as horny before and I wanted to savor the desire as long as I could stand the writhing of my vagina and my rising blood pressure before I moved toward satisfaction.

She leaned her mouth to my ear and whispered, "Long and slow, isn't that right?"

Weeks of observing Luminara were concentrated into one memory locked in the walls of my pelvis. When Lynn's fingers had slid into my vagina, I had clenched them. When she spoke to me I tried to swallow them.

I let go of the tub and slid down a bit. My head bobbed in and out of the water and I drew Lynn deeper into me. Then I grabbed her shoulders and hoisted myself up and pressed our wet and slippery breasts together. And we kissed until the top of my head buzzed and the ringing in my ears blocked out all other sound.

Still kissing me, Lynn tugged her fingers out of me and I almost came with the subsequent suck and rush of water. But I held on. I wanted more. She put her arms around me. She caressed my neck and ears and rubbed my back. She pulled out of our kiss and leaned back and put her hands, open-palmed on my breasts, then squeezed, then pinched my nipples, then held my breasts up and looked at them and smiled, then kissed them, then nibbled, then bit my nipples until I couldn't tell if I was feeling pain or pleasure. Until I was only feeling and I stopped thinking in words.

I locked my legs around her back and ran my hands over her breasts, down her ribs, around her hips, down and up her thighs, and docked them between her legs.

And then we rolled and wrestled in the water, fighting each other to top. We held each other under water for peaks of excitement. We lifted each other out of the water and licked and sucked and writhed until we folded and collapsed back into the water. She climbed my ribs with her fingertips like a boy shimmying up a tree. Her fingers and her toes probed and poked every opening to my body. I held them when I could, sucking and biting. And I put my own fingers in every orifice of hers. When I went inside her vagina she grabbed my wrist in her hand and pushed my whole fist into her. She arched her back and pumped herself up and down on it while I rubbed her belly with my other hand and stroked her clitoris with my tongue until her body shook and she pulled herself away from me.

Then she began to travel my body with her mouth, teasing me into wildness with a pause at a nipple, a suck, a bite, a nibble of an earlobe, a tongue-flick in an ear. Her hands held and squeezed and rubbed my buttocks, thighs, and belly. Fingers seemed to stray toward my vulva, but become distracted with something else and move on, over and over until I was ready to beg. I clamped myself to her knee and rode until finally she lifted me onto the side of the tub, spread my legs and went down on me as if she had known me my whole life. When I came I slipped back into the water. Lynn took her tongue away, but replaced it with her hand. I totally lost control of myself, and she had to hold my head out of the water or I would have drowned. I needed it that bad.

But the second I stopped spasming I sucked in big gulps of air and went all over Lynn. I went in and out of her, over and over, wrestling away when she tried to hold me inside. I pushed her breasts together until I could get both of her nipples in my mouth at once and sucked them as if to get milk, and she moaned and gasped and stuttered a lot of uh-uh-uhs. When Lynn came she cleaved to my body and suckled my breast like a baby. She gurgled and her hands waved in the air around my shoulders clenching and unclenching a dream I would never see. With one hand inside of her and a thumb on her clit, pumping more and more orgasm out of her, I clasped my other arm around her and shuddered with her until we were both done with long abstinences and virtual closet living.

Julio
MICKEY LASKIN

For the first few months of our relationship, my sexual identity and my body's desires hardly came up, except in the arena of learning how to be charming with the women, friendly with the men. I knew that Julio had lovers, but she never talked about them. For her part, she must have been aware that I was sexually frustrated and longing for release. Longing for release, but innocent, or only mildly soiled. Julio knew, and finally took pity on me; though when she began to address my sexual desires, it didn't feel like pity. It felt like a rite of passage, exhilarating and terrifying.

Julio started slow, with kisses and caresses on my lips and face. She had begun to bring up courting women, and sex, as topics of conversation. It was difficult, especially at first, to reveal my ignorance. But at appropriate points, my teacher would lean over and touch her lips to mine, sending a delicious chill down to my legs, or she would reach out and touch my cheekbone with the backs of her fingers, causing my head first to tilt a little away, then toward her hand, trying mindlessly to make contact again. As you may imagine, I began to be more aware than ever of my sexual energy, and sometimes walked around for whole days conscious of the moisture between my legs, and a slight ache of emptiness.

My tutorials progressed. The kisses and soft touches gave way to other sensations. Pinches on soft parts of my body, a wet tongue suddenly licking my ear or my jaw or neck. My breasts didn't escape Julio's demonstrations either. The first time was a terrible shock: one night, without warning, she pushed my body firmly onto the back of a park bench and grabbed both my nipples, one with each hand, and squeezed very tight, while pulling them—and me—toward her.

"Dani, *mi joven,* don't ever forget these." She twisted my nipples as she spoke and I tried not to gasp. "For men and women both, these are gifts for the beautiful but unpredictable *Oshún.* She loves to receive gifts, and she's apt to be generous in return if you offer them properly." Julio continued to hold my nipples, squeezing them to an internal rhythm, sometimes pulling, making my eyes tear and a cry escape my throat. Then she soothed the hurt by rubbing each nipple with her thumb, stroking, and with each stroke I could feel my legs get weaker. I took advantage of the bench at my back and leaned on it to help me keep my feet.

"If you know well the human body, Dani, you will have more access to your power. *Escúcha!* Listen to your own body, and when you touch someone else's, your fingers, your eyes, your ears, every sense you own should pay attention." Julio talked softly in my ear as she kept up the pressure on my body with her fingers. I didn't know if I would be permitted to try to escape, to ease the pain I was feeling now, traveling in waves from their two points of origin downward, invading my cunt and licking at my asshole, washing down my legs under my jeans and causing my knees to feel as if they would buckle at any moment. Then it stopped. She had eased open her fingers and was stroking my face, wiping away some sweat. Leaning into me, she whispered in my ear.

"Try another way to react, Dani. Many times we do better to stop resisting and repelling a situation. Stop fighting and accept your position—for the moment. You may call it *surrender,* but that word does not really describe properly the state of your mind or your body. *Give in; give it up;* these phrases may be more accurate. This giving up is like a gift and also an acceptance of a challenge. And accepting challenges is where we can grab our power and use it to our advantage. You will see what I am saying if you try it. Stop struggling and listen to your body, and to me." So saying, Julio kissed me gravely on the forehead and then lowered her mouth to my neck. I froze.

For a moment I felt the fear of death: a flutter like wings, traveling fast as light through my head, and my body shook. Her lips had come to rest on the most delicate part of my neck, down by my collarbone. Then Julio raised her head and looked me in the eye. "Remember, little one, what I just said." I looked at her face and tried to read her eyes as she could read mine. The flutter passed through me, and then something was released. I heard myself groan as she lowered her head again and I felt her teeth take my skin between them. For some timeless age I was clinging to her like a baby, my arms around her shoulders as she used her teeth like knives.

* * *

For days after this, I noticed an elevation of energy, a bounce in my step. I felt almost weightless. We didn't talk at all about my lesson in giving up resistance. I certainly didn't mention how sexually aroused I had been, how I was clinging to Julio partly from fear, partly from ecstasy. I caught her studying me surreptitiously now and then, but she didn't say anything either. Gradually I floated back to earth.

It was some time before Julio's next lesson, one which really did allow me my first true enlightenment. The difficulty of the lesson was commensurate with its bounty.

The fact is, a week or so after the lesson in the park, I found a girl-friend! Her name was Marilise, and I met her through Julio, who brought me one day on an errand to her neighbor Xiomara's house. Marilise was Xiomara's twenty-one-year-old daughter. We were attracted almost immediately, and I began to spend time with her, especially at parties. Our relationship continued, and this was a new and hopeful sign for me. Yet I was getting worried because we had not spent time alone yet, and I was trying to find a way to approach her; to put it baldly, to have sex with her. Julio watched and listened to us with interest and maybe a bit of amusement, though she never laughed at me. I didn't think I had much longer to figure out an approach that would be successful.

One night Julio finally took the matter into her own hands. She had told me the previous day that she wanted me to come home with her the next night. It wasn't unusual for me to be at her house, though I had only been on her patio and in the rooms on the first floor of the small, two-story house tucked into a corner of a dead-end street. But she had never asked me over late at night, preferring to walk me home when our evenings ended.

We walked into her house around midnight. Since her parents had been living for a while now with relations in the countryside, she lived alone. I was tired, and sat on the sofa while Julio did some work around the house. I didn't really notice what she was doing until she lit some scented candles on an altar, then used one of them to light other candles around the room until the room was bathed in their light. She turned on a tape deck, and ceremonial drums, punctuated by melodies and chants in *Lucumí,* filled the house.

I was almost asleep when something awakened my consciousness. I opened my eyes and saw Julio about four or five feet in front of me, looking happy. In her hand was a cigar, and the smell of its smoke, I realized, had disturbed my languor. She had taken off her shirt and her jeans, and was wearing only a pair of thin, white cotton shorts. Her feet, too, were bare.

"Welcome, Dani, to my house. Are you comfortable? We are going to go upstairs soon, and you will not be too afraid. Am I right? This is something for you, *mi querida*. You have wanted to ask me for so long, but you have not. I'm not sure whether to be pleased or angry at you for keeping silent. In one way I am pleased, since I believe you did not ask, preferring to defer to my decision on the timing of the matter. On the other hand, if your silence was due to a lack of trust or of embarrassment, I must admonish you that those feelings can be very dangerous. If you cannot trust your teacher, you cannot trust anyone, even the *orishas*. And why not trust me? After all, with your diligence, and my help, *Oshún* smiled on you the other night, Dani, that night when we offered you to her, first your body, then your soul. And she was kind, was she not? For look! You have a girlfriend now, and she is waiting. But she cannot be kept waiting any longer."

Julio came to me and lifted my body up, cradling me as one does an infant, holding me close to her chest. I smelled her clean smell, mixed with the harsh, acrid smoke from her cigar. She moved easily with me to stand in front of the altar. After speaking first softly and then louder in *Lucumí,* she put me down on my feet and took my hand and led me up the stairs.

Julio opened the door of her room. It was not a large one, and the window was covered by dark drapes. Like the living room, candles illuminated the space, casting quivering shadows on the walls with every breeze that wafted in from under the bottom of the drapes. I stood silently in front of her, until she pushed down on my shoulders and forced me to kneel. Now she stood in front of me, and she was humming and chanting, not continuously, but off and on. Her hand played in my hair, pulling it gently, until she finally seemed to finish some train of thought, or perhaps a part of her prayers.

"Dani, this is my ceremony. I want to make this clear, to you and to the gods, that it is my own, it has not been taught to me by *Oggún,* nor *Oshún* even. Not *Changó, Eleguá, Yemayá,* nor any of the others, this is mine. Its outcome is my responsibility alone. Close your eyes now, Dani, and give yourself to me. I will guide you in every step, and as you place yourself in my hands, know that you can only be doing this from the seat of your strength, the center of your power. When you cease resisting, you give a gift, and get one in return."

I closed my eyes. In the silence I waited, and all I could feel was my pulse like a powerful generator, flooding my body with energy and setting me aquiver like a taut wire. Then Julio's hand reached out and gathered the back of my neck and pulled my face into her crotch.

This was only the beginning. After a time, she helped me up and laid me on the bed. She took my clothes off and I was naked. My arousal became intense after many minutes of the most intimate caresses and kisses. And Julio was most generous, allowing me—no, *encouraging* me—to taste her, lick her, touch her. She, of course, did many things to *my* body, and since at some point I was told to open my eyes, I knew that her own eyes never left me. Often they demanded that even at the most intimate moment, my eyes stay on hers. I couldn't look away at those times, and this was perhaps the hardest part, for her eyes, locked into mine, made me feel truly exposed: that she could so easily see my pleasure.

Slowly, very slowly, although my arousal had peaked, receded, then peaked again, Julio was doing things to me that were firmer: rough things with her lips, like kissing me hard, pushing against my lips so that they were cut by my own teeth; invading my mouth with her tongue for long minutes until I was afraid I would not be able to take another breath. In fact, my head began to spin, my breath to come in gasps, my skin to flush from head to toe, bathing me in hot sweat.

At one point I was on my stomach beneath Julio, whose body covered mine, when I heard the door to the room open. When I tried to pick my head up and turn to look, Julio anticipated me and pushed my head back to the mattress, holding a forearm across my shoulders, grasping my head by the hair in one of her hands.

"Don't move." I felt myself wake up then, but I woke into the middle of a dream. Sometimes I felt many hands on my body, and sometimes they were gentle and sometimes harsh. At times I moaned with pleasure and other times groans tore at my throat. Once I recognized the sound of Marilise's voice, in response to a murmured question by Julio. Now I knew who had entered Julio's bedroom! But instead of relief, I felt a great thrill of fear. What was Julio doing to me? To us? Then it occurred to me that this must still be a dream. The idea made me **relax** again.

The candles were burning lower. Their scent, the heavy perfume of roses and musk, was so strong that it was like a veil in front of my eyes. Marilise was naked and she was lying on her back across the bed, her legs dangling over the edge from the knees down, her bare feet on the wood floor. I was hovering over her torso, cupping her soft breasts in my hands, kissing them, sucking at the nipples until she would pull my head up in order to kiss me. Julio had arranged us in this way, motioning me first to remove Marilise's dress, then moving our bodies until she seemed satisfied. My awareness was rising and falling, but it was always centered in my body, whose slightest oscillation I noticed immediately. I realized once that my skin was so sensitive, my nerve-endings so overloaded, that the lightest touch of Julio's fingernail running across my shoulder blades produced violent shivers exploding my body upward. And every cell in my own fingers was alive to the tissues under Marilise's skin. I had not known what a body could feel, really, until that night.

As I continued to play with Marilise, my body gradually melted over hers, so that after a while our legs were intertwined, my chest and stomach on hers, our hands all over each other. We were moaning too, and crying out sometimes. I almost failed to notice when I felt Julio's hands slip something around my body, around my waist and between my legs. It was a strap of some sort and there was something heavy on it in front, but the straps were already buckled before my hand got down to explore this object. I was puzzled when I felt it, and then it hit me! She had strapped a harness to my body and a large rubber phallus hung from it, between my legs where a boy's cock would be. I choked back my alarm and my body continued moving over Marilise.

My eyes were closed, my lips were on Marilise's neck, when I felt Julio lean over me. Her legs pushed against the backs of mine. One hand pressed down on the middle of my back. Beneath me, I felt Marilise shift, her body tautening because now she was bearing not only my weight as I lay on her, but Julio's as well. Julio's other hand held something sharp. I knew this because at the moment I heard her tell me to hold still, I felt it prick my skin on my right side. I don't think I could have moved then even if I wanted to, because somehow her one hand was exerting a tremendous force on my back, and her legs were jammed up tight against mine. I drew in my breath and held it. The sharp object was a knife. I knew because she told me as she moved its cold blade over my hot skin. My body remained still, but inside everything was vibrating.

Whenever the blade stopped and I felt it press into me, sometimes pricking, sometimes only scraping its cold hardness over me, my body would tense and then release from deep inside. If I screamed at any point, I wasn't conscious of it, but I must have, because several times Julio's hand moved from my back to my mouth and she covered it, murmuring soothingly in my ear. Marilise had begun to move more forcefully under me, her backside arching up from the mattress to push into my groin. Her eyes were sometimes open, but mostly they were shut and I became interested in making her open them. Like Julio, I wanted to see what was in her eyes.

I didn't notice right away when Julio put aside her knife. But when I did, I felt relief, not because I was no longer afraid, but because I could now move more freely. I really needed to move; the tension had built up in my body until I knew that the torture would end only when I could release it.

Julio took me by surprise. Quite literally, she took me. One minute every fiber in me was concentrating on the woman under me, and the next minute I felt something slim, warm and firm at my asshole. It stroked me there, and I began to wonder if I could hold on or if I would struggle with all my might to escape. She seemed to know what I was feeling, because she began to speak to me as her finger moved around my perineum.

"Ah! *Si*, Dani, yes! *Mi joven, mi niñito,* now is the time! Little one, you are about to lose your virginity. You will accept me down here, and you will thank me. You will not try to move away from me. You can't anyway, *jovencito.*" Julio's finger continued its probing, then it disappeared momentarily before I felt it again. It was wet now and somewhat slippery. The deeper in it went, the more it turned and stretched me, the louder became my groans, which I propelled, quite unknowingly, into Marilise's mouth.

When I finally thought I would slip into madness if Julio didn't stop, her finger once again left me. I held still, feeling hollowed, and waiting for whatever else she would do to me. Her finger did not return, but was instead replaced by something much bigger, much wider. I couldn't see what Julio had, though later, much later, I did. It was a hard, giant pod of some kind, from one of the trees that lined Havana's streets, flaming out huge flowers in brilliant tropical array. The pod's shell was dark brown, very smooth, and nearly ten inches in length, its diameter between an inch and two inches. In fact, it tapered to a fairly narrow end of about an inch, and it was this end she had introduced into my virgin ass. But that night, I could only feel it and I tried, I did try, even against Julio's orders, to move out of its reach. I failed, and only felt it slip in deeper as my trembling body cringed away.

At some point as she worked this amazing tool into me, Julio had also reached around my body and I felt her hand brush my body, felt warm liquid pouring from between my cuntlips. The touch was almost, though not quite, incidental to her real intention, which I soon recognized as I felt my new rubber cock being pulled forward. Now Marilise was thrusting her body up to mine and her moans gained a new intensity. I didn't understand what had caused this frenzy until her legs parted and she tried to bring them up around my hips. As if from a great height, or distance, I heard laughter. Julio's or the goddess *Oshún's,* I couldn't tell. Julio's hand then took one of mine and placed it around my cock, which was already halfway into Marilise.

"Hold it, use it, Dani. You are taking her now, as I will take you. *Escúchame, mi joven!* When you feel it's simply impossible to accept me for another second, then it's time to refocus your energy into a powerful force. Conquer your pain with a new understanding of what you are feeling. Let your body and mine guide you, and you will receive a great gift." So saying, Julio pressed down, using her body weight to thrust her tool deeper inside my bowels. Tears poured from my eyes at the immensity of the sensations, and I rode straight into Marilise as Julio began to fuck me in earnest. Our screams, mine and Marilise's, echoed inside my head until I heard nothing more.

The pond

VICKI LEWIS

People in town say that women wait for each other in the night, here in the park off Highway 9. This is the myth of my hometown. They say to come here late on Friday night. So on Friday night, I am here pushing through the damp brush. I come here half believing and wholly wanting the myth to be true. Women waiting for women here in this small town.

I sneaked out of my mama's house. Left her sleeping next to her police scanner crackling out emergencies and suspicions. She went to bed with the security that her only daughter was nestled on the couch in the next room. She does not know that I have women on my mind tonight. She does not know about my plan. I am a grown woman now, and I have secrets.

I drive my rattle-tailed hatchback to this park bordered with green cedar trees shadowed blue in the night. When I was a teen, I went fishing with my mom at the pond in the center of the park. Now I come here with sweaty palms and wide, searching eyes. I close the car door and slide my pride into my back pocket. I feel a little silly looking for action in this deserted park at one a.m., but curiosity leads my feet down the gravel path.

I don't know the codes, and I don't know the dress. I wear a blue Western snap shirt, tight black jeans, and boots. I hope that I stand out, and I hope that I fit in. I don't expect any big city dykes like me with slicked-back hair and silver jewelry. I expect callous-fingered women who scrape against the waist of this Bible-Belt town to reach for me with their hot-blooded hands.

I walk closer to the pond, where frogs belly out their screeching calls, where mosquitoes hang with appetites. The interstate buzzes in the distance. Musky August night air presses against my pulse. Thorny-tipped branches prick my palms. I smell nothing but cedar sap. I taste nothing but salt in the back of my throat. I am thirsty.

I feel eyes following me, breaking twigs with the weight of each step. Closer to the pond I creep. The eyes I've been feeling face me now, but her face is covered with a mask. Big green painted eyes, black and white slashes on each cheek. A red curled mouth. This is not Halloween or Mardi Gras. This mask is the code for women like me. She says nothing. And her silence holds me still. I hold my breath and stare into the eye holes of the mask and see black panthers leaping out. She is hungry and I am her prey. Her carved red mouth is smiling.

This is not what I expected, so I turn away. But she grabs me by the belt loops and knees me to the dirt. Mud under my fingernails. Gravel grinds under the tip of her boot as she rubs her hips against my back pockets. My pride melts into her thrusts. The insides of my jeans are soaked. She laces her thick, stubby fingers around my long skinny ones as she pushes me deeper into the wet earth.

She gets up on her hands and knees and whispers, "Turn over." I do what this stranger says. I don't care who this woman is. I just know that she wants me, and in her wanting I want her back. I roll over, and she rips off her T-shirt. Her heavy breasts hang over me like bait. I bite her burgundy nipples as hard as my teeth will clench without breaking blood. Her moan speaks my desire.

She works me out of my pants. The grass is warm and wet. Her hands solid and hot. She smells like the smoky tip of a match. She's lit me. My teeth lose grip of her breast when she slides two fingers inside me. Then three. She stares at me. This makes me nervous so I look at the crescent moon and listen for footsteps. I hear nothing but crickets chirping. We are alone. And I wonder if more women are doing this in other alcoves of this park.

Her hand circles my clit. I want to explode. Disappear. But instead I press her harder against my chest. Raise my knee to spread her legs. I bite her hard again. My teeth tame her to her side. She stretches out, facing me. I slink slowly down her body like a caterpillar. My bug eyes dart quickly from the edge of the piney brush that surrounds us to her writhing body underneath me. As long as we are quiet, I think, no one will find us. She does not seem afraid. My tongue oozes a slippery trail from her neck down to the path of dark curls leading to her cunt.

I unzip her zipper and clench her mound of hair. Tangled and wet. My hand rhymes her rhythm.

I don't want to see her face. Our bodies, not our identities matter. This is a matter of the flesh, of the pulse. Not of character. I stick my tongue into the carved red slit of her mask. She tastes of oak and ash. She unsnaps the pearl buttons of my shirt and slides it off my shoulders. She sucks my tit as her hands roam down my belly.

She whispers, "I've wanted you for years, Veronica. This is what I've always wanted."

My body pulls back. My body is still. She knows me. She knows my name. And I am stunted by the boundaries, by the syllables of my name. She knows my history. My family. The rumors. Everything I've tried to escape.

I hold still above her, bare-breasted in my desire and fear. I look over the hedges. The pond is still. I pull myself off this woman who knows my name. Climb over the hedges and dive into the pond. Half-hoping she will follow. Half-hoping the ripples will mask me.

Bread from a stone

Donna Allegra

Blaze is giddy with excitement, eyeing all the femmes in the room. This bar feels like an old-time dyke scene where butches are butches and femmes are up front about where they're at. Blaze and I enter as buddies, two butches out for a night on the town in a strange city. I wear Lee jeans, my Wrangler jacket, Fila high-tops. She's in 501's, black engineer boots, white tee under her black leather jacket.

"Look at all these cute girls, Evan. Babes in Toyland just for me," she crows.

I look at her as if amused. "Half for you, half for me," I correct her.

"Oh yeah, friends share and share alike," she says grudgingly and takes a pull from her Classic Coke bottle.

This is why we're supposed to be here: to meet someone, go home with her, and tell each other about it afterwards.

"Wanna dance?"

"Not yet," she begs off. I feel tender for her in this shyness and there's nothing I can do to help her loosen up any quicker.

"I'll be back," I say, and saunter to the center of the room to set off a boogie. I sort of join a group of women dancing around each other. I feel some performance anxiety about getting up to dance, which is the other reason people come to a club. I want to be the best dancer on the floor to keep Blaze looking at me. Her eyes can narrow in admiration or in envy, I don't care which, but I want to be the center of her attention.

I feel women checking me as a hot-looking butch. Blaze's intelligence works an aphrodisiac on me, but I know my physical surety allures women. I open myself to the promise of the night: warm bodies, heated energy and desire fermenting in the air. My sex appeal is resonating and I wonder, am I attractive to women in the ways that they're attractive to me? I've spent too long a time on the unrequited side of longing. I need this groove with lesbians where my body is responded to.

The woman trying to imitate my moves thinks she's doing something, but she's dorky and comes off lame. She makes me look good, though. I wink over to where Blaze straddles the back of her chair and dangles the Coke bottle from her hand.

Secretly I watch Blaze with a mixture of hostility and affection. I like seeing her awkwardness but it's yearning that fuels my judgment. I still nurse a pot on the back burner and its bubbles haven't broken the surface yet.

I don't know when will ever be a good time to approach her. I'd wanted us to be alone, some place quiet, a Saturday evening and then the night to ourselves. But Blaze wanted to party.

"This makes three years sober, we are on vacation in a new town and nobody knows us, Evan. It's perfect for taking a chance on yourself. You, Miss Thing, can try to make some noise for a change and I can lighten up." She could laugh then about each of our weak points.

"Yeah," I said, not really wanting to get it on like that.

"Don't worry," she quickly turned conciliatory, reassuring me. "Nobody's going to bite you. If you get tongue-tied, I'll pick up the slack."

I felt like a sullen spoil-sport. She was close enough to kiss me, but that'd never occur to her.

"And to be on the safe side, here's a good luck present."

She pulled a square of plastic packaging from her jeans and pressed it into my hand. I looked at it and jumped away as if she'd tried to light me with a match.

"I don't need that," I yelped like a tomboy unwrapping a Barbie.

"Take it, Evan. It's the pre-moistened kind you like."

When Blaze first stopped drinking, it was hard to hang out in the ways we used to, like going to a bar or having a beer at somebody's house. I'd hated it when she was drunk, stupid and wasted. I was glad to see her sober, but for a long time I didn't know how to be with her not drinking. She still had her strong spirit and the backbone to uphold it. We had to discover ways to do friendship different. Now, it's better—I have a shot at keeping things cooking between us.

Technically, I still drink, but not much. When Blaze was newly sober, I'd order fake beers, to keep up my image with the crowd. After awhile, I dropped the pretense. I never liked drinking piss.

As I return to the table where Blaze and I had settled ourselves, I see a high femme standing there, her stance all seductive promise. Damn, all it takes is for me to turn my back for a minute before Blaze starts kicking some game. The woman is just her type—wears an A-line mini skirt, legs up to her tits and cleavage down to her navel. Lipstick, but no nail polish or claws at the end of her cuticles.

I might as well hang it up for the evening. This femme will have Blaze humming in no time. She's a nice big-sized girl, her color a pungent mix of cinnamon and ginger-tinted skin. She seems like a star in a movie scene. Twenty-feet tall, in Panavision with quadraphonic sound. You'd have to pay hard cash to see her for a couple of hours, a limited run.

I feel I'll come across as a character from a TV show—smaller than a kindergarten kid, saddled with commercial interruptions, and can be turned off at any minute with a remote control click. Still, I pride myself up to get back to my seat. I tell myself I shouldn't trip on what Blaze ends up doing with this woman. This is what we're here for, right? To pick up girls, get laid, and tell each other the story afterwards.

I draft a smile for the femme rooster and see that Blaze is being a butch kitten. She's not flirting hard, just playing.

"Thanks for making me move," Blaze says as I squeeze in towards my seat. She doesn't really move. She makes me press against her to get my spot inside the booth. I feel warmth rise from her body like the breath off a toasted muffin. She introduces me to the woman, singing my praises.

"Strong, silent, and guaranteed to dance your ass off."

It makes me feel goofy when Blaze goes on about me like that.

The lady isn't biting. She points to a questionnaire that's been on our table and magically comes into view. She turns to me and explains, "The management is conducting a demographics poll." She turns her chest appeal to Blaze and says, "Would you take just a few minutes to fill this out for me, hon?" She leaves the questionnaire on the table, her perfumed scent in the air, an eager grin on Blaze's face.

"Highest level of education completed," Blaze pronounces.

"Kindie garden."

"Sex."

"Yes, please. No, better not. I get it at home."

"Male or female are your options, Evan." She tries to sound unimpressed, but a smile dimples from her cheek.

"This is a matter of controversy, I can't take sides on the issue."

"Age?" she asks.

"It varies with my emotional state."

"Oooh, here's a baddie: *How many beers do you drink per week?* I'm exempt on that one."

"Yeah, me too these days. None," I conclude.

"What's your favorite brand?" she reads, irritation crusting an edge in her tone.

"See above," I say, alerted that the alcohol culture is getting to her.

"How many packs of cigarettes do you smoke per week?"

"None."

"What's your favorite brand?"

"Oh my. I can see you never passed common sense."

Her smile returns and I want to keep her laughing and jovial. "How many times do I have to tell you to pay attention? Take notes, Blaze, there'll be a quiz later."

"See, you can rap and be funny, Evan. Let other people in on it sometimes, not just me. Don't you want to have cute girls squeal over you?"

"That'd be lesbian heaven."

She looks like the father of the bride giving his daughter away—supposed to be glad, but not. This is what I want from her.

When she gave up drinking so much—"Got sober," is how she corrects me—I felt different about her. I remembered how I'd first hoped it would be between us before we fell into being ace boon coons. I wanted us to be much more than pals.

She's softer now, someone can get inside her. I just don't know how to jump the track we've been running and take us to a different place.

The high femme returns, is professionally unfriendly as she takes the survey from us, doesn't give up her name and leaves. I'm glad she was just doing her job.

"Don't waste your time, kid," and I put my arm around Blaze by way of consolation.

"You can't fail if you don't try. That's what I keep trying to show you," Blaze says.

"So now I can have you all to myself," I say. Then to cover it up, "Is that your body oil I keep smelling?" I put my nose to her neck and feel her lush-friendly skin.

Blaze turns into the arm I'd put around her shoulder to give comfort, turns in a way I don't expect. She's hugging me. The corner she's turned takes us to a place where I feel the cooking between my legs rattling the cover off the kettle. I strain to hear her say, "You've always had me. This is as real as it gets."

I hold her head to my face and I'm the only woman in the room who knows how silken her dreads feel. Her warm breath in my face has the fragrance of newly born bread. I kiss her mouth that tastes like uncooked dough.

I pull slightly away. "I can't say I was drunk," I joke, to leaven her judgment call.

"Don't even try," she whispers. She draws my mouth back to her, tries to swallow my tongue and drinks my saliva. We change from a moist grainy mixture to a new creature fresh from the oven. We'll tell each other about it later.

wives

Heather Lewis

I got out of there, out of Beth's office. I went directly home, and once there tried not to think of the only thing I could think of, which was when could I have her again.

It was a Friday, so I should've been going to work the next morning. I knew this much, though it didn't exactly mean I'd do anything about it.

When it came time, I called in sick, not realizing until afterwards that I'd done the same thing the week before. Realized maybe I ought to begin worrying what they would think. I already didn't make enough there and I hadn't been making money any other way lately. Something needed to change.

I lay in bed and tried to convince myself Beth only meant trouble. That the thing to do was get away from her. Thinking this left me thinking about her, though. And once I'd begun that, the will to leave her didn't last long.

I told myself my concern was practical, simply about legalities. That I needed to keep seeing her to meet the terms of my probation. This was thin enough that even I could see through it—they could assign me another therapist. Still I tried to stay on this plain. Not drift into thinking about how she could make me feel, when she wanted to, which didn't seem often enough.

I couldn't face calling her. Spent the day—Saturday—avoiding this impulse. Finally went out to avoid it because I couldn't stand that she might play cool and aloof and impossible. That this weekend might completely match the last one, with me ordering myself around her, running to her and not knowing how I'd find her. I already had this sense that she took up too much of my life, or maybe all of it. And right when I needed badly for this not to be true I ran into Burt.

This was not a hard thing to do. It was only a matter of going to certain places at certain times. And so I did these things believing I had no plan in mind.

He was at that same bar, with Jeremy this time. And I'd seen his car in the lot with the same guy waiting behind the wheel.

They sat me down at their table. Began buying me drinks and all through this I had that same nagging sense of wondering just what they wanted me for. They weren't talking to me really, not exactly. I was just there listening to them and then they got up and we all went out and they gave me a ride home, which was good since I still wasn't driving my car.

This put me pretty much where I'd been, only later and drunk, and so my resolve was nowhere and I found myself calling Beth. She sounded sleepy and irritable but not quite surprised and so I couldn't help but feel she'd won.

I didn't ask to see her, it seemed the only way to preserve some kind of dignity. This seemed to confuse her, and after all I hadn't called with anything else in mind so we stumbled around a while with her finally saying, "Why don't you meet me at noon."

She said it in this in-between way that almost made me say where, and besides her office seemed too small and not right. We didn't say any more and I went to sleep feeling, well, *happy* is not quite the word but *secure* maybe. *Drunk,* anyway.

I woke up later than I'd intended and with the sense of having made a mistake. I thought quite seriously of standing her up. Really wanted to, though the motive was filmy, hard to determine, harder to act on.

I arrived at her office disheveled and discouraged. She'd gotten there already and she came out to the waiting room and took my arm in a way that reminded me we hadn't always been like this, and when we went into her room we both sat down. I felt oddly comforted by this, unsure now what I wanted from her and she seemed that way too, tentative and different than she'd been in a long while.

I didn't say anything but found myself looking at her intently. Meeting her eyes for what seemed like a long time. Then I noticed what I was doing and so my eyes found the floor and stayed there. And when she spoke, when she said, "Are you all right these days?" the sound of her voice—any noise really would've startled me.

I didn't know how she meant this. How widely she meant. How much ground I was allowed to cover if I answered. The easy thing would've been to say, yes, I'm fine, but this was so far from true I couldn't shape the words. What I said instead was, "I don't really think so."

I looked at her when I said it and wished I hadn't because it seemed to have hurt her. She maybe had wanted the other answer. How could I know what she wanted? And I was so weary of trying to know what was in her head and of her never letting on. This last thing maybe provoked me to say, "Are you?"

Her face changed again. She looked like she'd no idea what I'd said and so quickly I added, "all right, I mean."

Her eyes went cloudy and then teared and my own vision blurred from the same things and we just sat there staring at each other.

I wondered the way through this, how to come out the other side and quickly. But just when I thought I'd be unable to stand this another moment, it grew sweet and I felt a closeness I hadn't felt in what had to be months. And while this took over my body, while this sweetness roamed my chest and then the rest of me, taking hold in my limbs, I willed my brain to keep out of it, to stay still and not wreck it, not start me pumping to leave or push this toward sex because of course those escapes were there too, always there and calling.

She didn't fidget, and she didn't look away. But she didn't say anything either. Not for the longest time. And then finally what she said was, "I'm afraid I'm not helping you."

I couldn't imagine how she meant this. I wanted to laugh, but she seemed genuine. Seemed not at all to see the absurdity of what she'd just said. This left me lightheaded, nearly giddy. Unsure I could keep hold of what seemed maybe like anger.

There was so much room here for nastiness, for sarcasm. The only thing stopping me was the look on her face, still truthful and gentle. To meet that with cruelty seemed just wrong. What I did instead was stall. I said, "How do you mean?" And I truly wanted to know because the eeriest thing was the way I could never tell if she acknowledged all of what went on with us or if she kept it too far buried.

"I think you're getting into trouble."

I wondered if she was talking about herself more than me—if she meant I was getting her into trouble—because now her eyes left mine and stared out the window until this began to feel like all the other times she'd tried to keep herself away from me.

"How?" I asked her.

"You're going back to it."

"Not really, not that much. Not lately."

"Weren't you just last night?"

This threw me. And when she looked back at me her eyes looked sore. I found myself trying very hard to see what she was saying in some other way than that she'd gone looking for me.

At first I thought she'd maybe seen my car in the parking lot. Made her conclusions from there, but then I realized I hadn't been using it and so what did that mean? That she'd actually been in that bar last night?

"I tried calling you," she said. "I wanted to see if you were okay. I hadn't heard from you. I was worried, and so I went by your place but there were no lights, and you didn't answer but your car was there."

She stopped here like this was too painstaking, too time-consuming. Her eyes drifted away and when she started again she said, "I saw you with those men."

She said all of this like it made sense. Like what she'd done was the most ordinary thing for a person to do. It was hard not to go along with her. Not to feel that yes, of course, she's the one who knows what she's doing.

I kept my head just above water. I said, "What is it you think you saw?"

"I saw you get in a car with them."

I wanted her to look at me, wanted to get her to, because all I could see was her sitting in her car in that lot watching for me. I couldn't stand what this had me wondering and it made me plainer than usual. I said, "Look at me," but when she did she seemed to almost be crying and so now I looked away.

"So you thought up the rest of it, made it up."

"Should I have stayed and watched?"

I wanted to say, "What were you doing there in the first place?" because this all gave me too much to sort through. I felt both unnerved and afraid of her, and at the same time cared for—that she would go to such lengths, but out of what?

"They drove me home."

"Oh, and that's better?"

"No, that's it. That's all of it." I said this not quite understanding how quickly I'd become the one defending my actions, though it served both of us. Let her stay above question and let me not think what the questions should be.

I stole a look at her and then another and when I was sure she'd got hold of herself I kept looking. This put us back to staring at each other, which started hard and almost mean before it went gauzy. I wouldn't touch her. I kept telling myself this over and over in my head until I believed it, but I began to see leaving as the only way to ensure it.

It wasn't me, but something about her that demanded I do this. I don't mean how it usually went, with her telling me to. This instead felt like, "Get out before it's too late, this time might really hurt."

I did leave, and she didn't stop me. But I went home to find something I'd never have expected. Inside my building, just outside my door, Ingrid was sitting on the steps. The sight of her took away whatever will I'd ever had with her. And then with Beth at my back, the sight of Ingrid felt like relief.

We went inside and she stayed standing near the door, sort of hovering there like she didn't know any better than me why she'd come. I put my keys down. I took off my shoes without thinking because my feet had begun to hurt from all the walking I'd been doing.

I sat on the couch and waited. Ingrid finally sat down, but she kept her coat on; looked confused with me or herself, I couldn't know. Something looked even more wrong than usual and this made me reach over and pull her coat from her shoulders, pull her toward me and I held onto her while she cried, and I kissed her hair and just held her.

I didn't think I wanted to know what had happened—what on earth could've put her in the head to come here. I knew we'd wind up in the bedroom but I hoped it'd take a while because I was afraid what I might find on her body.

It was bruises, all along her left side. The kind you get from someone getting you down on the floor and kicking. She never said how, never explained it at all, but then I suppose that's what I offered, someone she could go to without explanation. Someone who'd just simply know and know exactly.

We didn't really do anything more than lie around with each other. Finally I went to find some ice for her, though being only as far away as the kitchen gave me the distance to ask what jeopardy she'd put me in by coming here. And if she began making a habit of it? This appealed to me even as it frightened me.

I went back to her. Laid a towel on her side and then the ice and then put some pillows around her and all of this began me thinking about the way it'd been in their house. The way it had worked with her and me and her husband. Her cleaning up the mess he'd made of me, taking care of me afterwards. And through the same kind of logic people seem to know me for and even count on, I began to feel I owed her this. That she'd do the same for me. That she already had.

In the morning, I had trouble with Ingrid even being there. I got up, took away the towel, now soggy and cold. I did these things trying not to wake her and she went along with this, seemed dead to anything I might do and I was glad for it.

I needed some time by myself. I needed at least to figure out what day it was and where I should be. It felt like Sunday but knowing it wasn't did nothing to put me in motion.

It was late enough that the phone began ringing and I knew it'd be my boss at the store trying to find me. That was about the last thing I could see dealing with so I unplugged the phone. Decided right then I wouldn't go back to that job.

This meant having the day with Ingrid. Maybe it did. After all I didn't know her plans. How long she expected to stay. I'd remained in an in-between of not wanting her there and feeling closed in, but at the same time afraid of her leaving, not for her but for me. Afraid of being alone with myself in a way that might make me sort through the things I was doing.

Ingrid did stay. She spent the day in bed, not really ever awake. I waited on the couch, realizing finally that what I was missing were my afternoon drinks, the ones that usually started at lunch. I pulled out a bottle and a glass and lay there drinking awhile, watching Ingrid through the bedroom door.

About when I was getting dressed to go see Beth, Ingrid got up and went into the bathroom. And after a while of her being in there I heard water running, heard what sounded like her getting into the tub and I went in to brush my teeth.

"I have to go out for a bit," I told her. And though she looked stricken, she pulled back from this I guess because her voice was steady when she said, "Would it be all right for me to stay here a few days?"

I considered this, knowing I would never refuse, but that alone wasn't enough to keep from figuring out where it'd put me. Having her here while I went back to work for real in the parking lot? The way this would up the chances of her husband showing up looking for me. Or sending someone else to do it.

"You can stay as long as you need.... As along as you want." This was what I finally told her. And when I began my walk to Beth's I saw my car as I passed the little lot by my building. I wondered if I should move it, put it somewhere else. Whether it could be something that would tip Ingrid's husband all the faster to my whereabouts. But then of course I knew he'd find us easily whenever he bothered to try.

I got to Beth's still edgy and distracted. I couldn't tell how she was and it seemed forever since I'd seen her, what with all that had come in-between. She looked different to me, but then she did look different during the week. More distant and composed even if just on the surface.

"You didn't go to work again."

She said this just as a statement of fact, while I was still standing. Running my fingers over a glass paperweight full of trapped, dead flowers. This object sat on her desk and I surprised myself to notice this meant I was standing right behind her—something I'd never done before.

She didn't turn to look at me when she talked. Instead she looked straight ahead. Looked at the chair where I ought to be sitting, and I might've sat down if I didn't know that soon as I did she'd find anything else to look at but me.

Having Ingrid in my home gave me some kind of false something. I guess bravado, because I felt less like I needed Beth, though I suppose really I needed her more, if only she'd ever been someone I could talk to.

I'd moved quickly to the other side of what I'd just been feeling. Began feeling so swiftly small and afraid that I did sit down and when I did I astonished myself. I said, "I think I'm in trouble."

She looked at me, for real she did. She said, "Tell me what's happened."

I had enough sense to know I couldn't do that, not exactly. I said, "I can't go back to that job. There's some way I just can't. There's too much else..."

I expected a lecture, something standard she'd shift into from habit but instead she said, "Do you want to do the other thing more?"

"No, I don't think so. I don't know. I just know I can't play store any longer. I don't belong there. I don't know who I am there because I'm never there, not really, not me."

"You belong where?"

"I don't know. Maybe the hooking suits me better. It's all clearer."

I didn't know why I was saying these things to her and I believed I'd better stop because it seemed dangerous. She seemed dangerous if I let on what really went on inside me.

I waited for her to argue with me but she didn't, she said, "Why do you think that?"

"Because I know what **to do,** what's expected of me." And then I thought of Burt and said, "Most of the time, anyway."

I sat there unable to say anything more, and as I looked at her, this longing for her seeped into every space in me. It gave me a strange solid feel, but with a weight to it. I didn't believe I could get to my feet if I tried. But she was on hers and holding her hand out to me, and when we walked to her car, she kept her arm around my waist and I leaned into her and the heaviness of my body just felt pleasant.

She drove us to a park near her house. No one much was there, it being later than dusk and cold out. I pulled the coat she'd given me tighter around me and it was odd to be among swings and slides, things children play on, but the cold air felt good and she felt good, still with her arms around me, still guiding me around. The sweetness of all of this made me want to cry and the funny thing of it was that's what I did.

I cried in her arms for what seemed forever until I really couldn't stand up anymore. And so we sat on top of a picnic table, her still with her arms wrapped around me. And then it somehow seemed time to get back in the car. I wanted her to turn down the street to her house but she didn't. She drove me home.

My place did make more sense, what with her having a husband, but then here I was with someone else's wife, so what could I do? She said, "Will you be all right? Do you want me to come in with you?"

And of course I did. I wanted her more in that moment than maybe I ever had. And Ingrid upstairs? I couldn't tell Beth about that. There was nothing to do. I said, "No, I'll be okay. I'm all right." And then I said, "Thanks." And before I got out of the car I put my arms around her neck and held on for a little bit, and when I went up my stairs I felt okay again. For a little while I really did.

Ingrid was on the couch and dressed. She really did look like a wife all of a sudden and she'd somehow fixed us dinner, or bought it somewhere and so we ate and had some drinks and it began to seem normal to have her there. And though I'm not proud of it, it crossed my mind she might take care of money for me for a while. Postpone my having to go out again.

We were drinking still and smoking and the phone rang and my instinct of course was not to answer it, except for knowing it was Beth.

I picked it up and she said, "I just wanted to make sure you're all right."

I walked with the phone into the bedroom and closed the door to Ingrid, but I still couldn't shift gears so fast. I felt the jerky guiltiness in my voice when I said, "I'm okay, really." And everything about the way I was speaking made plain my impatience. She couldn't know why, just sounded sort of confused and what she wound up saying was, "Tomorrow, why don't you come later than we said."

"When?"

"Six, I guess. That would be better I think. I have a full day and..."

She didn't bother to finish as if she remembered who she was talking to.

"Six is fine," I said. "I have some things to do, too," and I didn't know why I said this last thing and wished I hadn't.

"Oh," she said. "All right. Six, then." And I felt her lingering and it felt brutish to edge toward hanging up, but in another awful way it seemed to be working in my favor.

"Okay, I'll see you then," I said. And then I hung up the phone and went back to Ingrid.

She still sat on the couch, smoking a cigarette, staring at her drink on the coffee table.

"Who was that?" she asked like she'd had years of practice, which of course she had.

It startled us both though. Her more than me because she quickly said, "I'm sorry. I don't know why I said that. It's none of my business."

I didn't attempt to explain, though a part of me wanted to. Here I was again with all this inside me I wanted to tell but with the absolute wrong person to tell it to.

Instead I held out my hand and she took it. We went into the bedroom, me not knowing who I wanted exactly, only knowing too clearly it was Beth who'd started me needing someone.

Ingrid and I lay down together, and it seemed at first it might be like last night, with us just lying around, and, in a funny way, recognizing that this was maybe most what I wanted from Beth, or would've tonight anyway, this drove me past it. I couldn't lie there thinking about her. If I did, it might start me crying again, from that same place I didn't understand, and that'd give Ingrid all the wrong sorts of ideas of me. I'd be the last thing she'd want.

I undressed her and then undressed myself and she turned the covers down on the bed she must've made and I wondered at what I was doing, not just this minute but with the whole of my life. Wondered how I'd come here and from where.

These thoughts must've stopped me entirely because I heard Ingrid's voice. Heard her say, "Nina, what is it? What's the matter?"

And I discovered myself standing stock still by the bed, but breathing hard and what I was wishing was that I'd told her my real name because maybe then I'd feel like we knew each other.

"Nothing," I said as I got under the covers with her. But it wasn't going to work. I could tell this already; couldn't get rid of all the things I was thinking and when she began to touch me, at first just my neck, stroking a line under my jaw, then I knew I'd never keep from the feelings either. And so with neither my mind or my body a safe place to be I looked to her body. Turned toward her and began touching her in return and for a short while this worked.

I kissed her shoulders and then her breasts. Did these things until all I felt anymore was her and not me. And this lasted until I pulled the covers back, saw the bruises on her side, by now purpley and still reddish.

The sight of them caught me up, nearly stopped me, and for an instant it ran through my mind to ask her how it'd happened. But I knew this too was about me. About keeping me from myself and I knew it wouldn't work and besides I knew exactly how she'd come to be hurt in this way. Could see it all—her on the floor and him kicking her—and I knew that the one or two times I'd had this done to me I'd felt the least human of all.

To make her revisit this just to spare myself, this seemed close to something he'd do. Instead I put a pillow behind her so she wouldn't have to lie flat, and she sank against it while I wrapped my arm around her thigh.

I kissed her forever—her belly, her thighs—and I felt her hands in my hair, heard her saying little things, murmuring in a way I couldn't make out and didn't quite want to, afraid it might sound too much like what Beth said. And if they were both saying the same kinds of things, how could I believe either one of them? How could it be any more than the things people say when they're together like this? And this was made all the more tangled by my wanting to believe Beth but not Ingrid.

So in this way I came back to Beth just as I got inside Ingrid. And I listened to Ingrid now because it was only sounds and breaths and my own breathing was changing but not in the right way. In a way that forced me to take my mouth from her and just fuck her and try to choke off my own sounds, which might end up in sobs if I didn't get hold of myself.

Ingrid tried to turn—first toward her bruises but crying out when that hurt, and so she turned toward me. I pulled another pillow, let her onto her stomach, got myself up and behind her, got my hand back inside her, with her asking all this time now for more of me, of my hand.

I grew afraid of myself in this, afraid I'd get carried away, carried off to where she wanted me to go and then I stopped worrying this.

I fucked her until she was the one crying—out of a place I both knew and didn't because usually when she got here she stayed silent and away from me. But this time, when I was starting to stop, she cried at me to keep on. She said, "Please, don't. Please don't leave me."

She'd never said anything like this and so I listened. I put my hand further into her and held it there, tried to get further inside and she held herself very still and then I did this too, I held her, still with my hand there, stayed just this way until she turned again, toward me, and her face looked a way I'd never seen. She looked young and afraid and I opened my arms and she held on.

It was a long time before she quieted. I felt helpless. Thought of all the stupid things to do—bring her a drink, a cigarette. I kept myself from doing these things until she got to the place of asking me to, and then I was glad to have actual tasks. To be able to get up from that bed.

I brought these things back with me—the bottle, our glasses. Made a separate trip for the cigarettes just to have more time with myself. I tried to drink the way she did—in the long swallows that were helping her—but for me it just brought back the choking, and the cigarette I tried did this too, even more. I stubbed it out halfway finished and that's when she noticed me.

She curled up near me and put her hand between my legs and I lay back, opened my legs because she told me to, and it felt like what I wanted.

She stroked me and stroked me and I felt a calmness begin near her hand and then follow it. She trailed her fingers up my body to my throat and back down, and I couldn't not know Beth had done this too, and not so long ago. And so I wondered, what is it about me that lets women know to do this?

My breathing grew steadier and deeper and she talked to me in a way that said nothing. She said things like, "There, now. You're all right. Sweetheart, everything's all right." And I could see how it wasn't because I'd begun to believe her and when she put her hand in me I couldn't be anywhere else but with her. Couldn't do anything but feel what she was doing. And it was all slow and gentle and I wanted more of her than I could take. Tried hard to ask for her but now I was the one who could only make sounds and cries.

She knew anyway. We were enough alike in these ways and so I felt her get very far into me and felt myself close around her, wanted to put my legs around her too but couldn't move them. I felt limp and wonderfully exhausted, so slack and peaceful and she seemed to find comfort in this because when I looked she was smiling. Not in a large way, but this small change in her face that I hadn't seen in a long while, or maybe ever.

She took her hand from me slowly, let it stay underneath her when she sank into me. And I felt her hand and the weight of her body as indistinguishable things. And I came in this way, too, a way that made it hard to make out what was what, and who was who. But all that really mattered right then was that somebody was holding me.

like a virgin
DOLPHIN JULIA TRAHAN

I never lost my virginity. I ditched it seventeen days before my sixteenth birthday. *Sweet sixteen and never been....* No way.

Bob, a red-headed, twenty-five-year-old drifter, was my first taste of forbidden fruit. I feasted, then told him to get lost.

At eighteen, I literally dove head first into Beth. She was an older woman and drove a hot-red sports car. The first time we had sex, she came so hard, I peed my pants.

I'm pretty much an average kind of a straight dude. Ambitious, but average. Once I got over the stumbling blocks, I began to make love to as many women as possible.

There were amazing honeymoons, but I escaped marriage. I'm extremely lucky. Especially since, in my spontaneity, I rarely used protection.

That's where Julie comes in. She's the girl that rejuvenated my innocence.

I met her about two years ago. She's a late-forties, bisexual, femmy-type and real bossy in that rich, white way. She always called me Darlin' and Honey. When she told me, "Men travel from all over the world to have sex with me," I knew she was my girl.

Well, she wasn't really my girl, so I wanted to play it safe. Take it slow. See, I wanted to do things different this time. I learned the hard way that running to the new, exciting person, place or thing is often the same as running away.

I used to think I knew myself pretty well: a sensitive poet, a lonesome spirit, a romantic hero. But when I was twenty-four, my mind started screaming things I had never heard before. I saw images of horrific events—once cast-off with bravado—that blew away my faith in humankind. The irony of the cruel joke didn't escape me. Under the right circumstances, a whiff of perfume or feminine chatter sent me from confident crip to terrified little girl.

Now, being a regular guy, I think best with my head. I started hanging out with some Bay Area lusty ladies, hoping to exorcise these molesting monsters while keeping a hand in the action.

I wasn't prepared for waking up to broken Christmas presents under the tree. Instead of gang bangs and cheesecake, I got: "I'm looking at your arms to see what you can manage." To which I replied, "Jerry Lewis doesn't get me hot and neither do you." When my prissy butch girlfriend of eleven months cried out in ecstasy, "You might be disabled, but you're great in bed," I decided to take matters into my own hands.

Sex is powerful, magical action. Good sex creates good life. Bad sex creates misery and hatred. I have a short time on Earth. I don't have time for misery or bad sex. I decided to see a sex surrogate.

This is the same story I told Julie when I first visited her Pacific Heights apartment. Only I cried more than talked. She sat like a job interviewer, taking notes with a purple felt tip while I despaired about how I had lost enjoyment in my body. I fired off a list of my sexual abuses, including those normal medical procedures that weren't so normal and the statistics I knew by heart. Did you know that eighty percent of permanently disabled kids are abused? I told her I refused to have sex with any more partners who told me I'd be better off if I was nondisabled. I was scared to come with other people cuz that's when the tears and helplessness came. My life was a lie. My lovers resented me. I was tired of numbing out during sex. I just wanted to quit having panic attacks. But how was I supposed to replenish my over-charged battery pack when I only found girls who assumed I liked my lube from a tin cup?

Maybe this was a bad idea. Was this the woman who was going to put the lemon back into my squirt? Dr. Ruth says women reach their sexual peak during their mid-thirties, so I figure thirty-four to thirty-seven year olds are the hottest. Julie wasn't dried up or ugly or anything, but she was a little too skinny, and she didn't laugh at my jokes. Her head was oddly shaped, kinda like a poker chip.

I realized I better just shut up and let Julie tell me how she worked. I must've been staring cuz she interrupted herself and said with big sad eyes, "Don't make fun of my face." My heart broke for her. I forgot all my problems. I didn't know what to say. She assured, "I think I can help you." I made another appointment.

In the beginning, we talked a lot and held hands. I told her I did this with my talk therapist, who's name was also Julie. She was also a Jewish femmy semi-straight girl. I liked sex-surrogate Julie better because she gave me advice and homework and didn't try to "correct" my point of view about my life. She even encouraged me to do a kind of trauma therapy that works with hardcore Vietnam vets and tough cookies like me.

She listened to my frustrations and always had a common sense way out. But we were out of sync. She kept trying to teach me the proper steps of dating etiquette. What did she think I was? A virgin? Ninety bucks an hour for sex with a goody two shoes. No way. I walked out and never called her again.

* * *

Life spun on a razor blade. Hopeless about ever finding relief from flashbacks, I started undressing for my talk therapist. She had stopped charging me long before that. I lost pints of blood in those months. If I wasn't hurting myself, some other woman was. My writing and performance were beginning to receive national attention. The BBC recognized me as "a pioneer artist in disability culture." Was I a rising star, treading water, or just drowning?

I called sex-surrogate Julie. "Would you still work with me? I need to work more on flashbacks and orgasms."

She said yes, but she was in a serious relationship and would only be having sex with clients for another two months. We agreed that my orgasm was of the utmost priority. I needed less chat, more action. She called me later to ask if we could have one session where we just talked—she wouldn't charge me. I thought that was really sweet.

I brought her a carnation and tried to be more honest. I told her that I was scared because I didn't want any more cold sex. She asked me how I wanted to be treated. I said, "I just want it to be okay to be me. Y'know, I don't want you to treat me like I'm weak or stupid cuz I've been hurt a lot, but I don't want to pretend that betrayal isn't part of me."

When I saw her the next session, we talked more, then quickly undressed and hopped onto the bed. She rubbed my thighs until I thought I would burst if I didn't get relief soon. She hopped out of bed and disappeared into the bathroom.

It was so inconsiderate. When she returned I asked, "Why didn't you fuck me?"

"I didn't want to hurt you. I didn't know what you liked."

"Come here," I demanded. "I'll show you what I like."

I spread her wide on the bed, slipped on a glove, and started pumping as hard as I could. She melted and dug her head into the pillow. After a while, I realized I was paying ninety dollars for the privilege of hand-fucking this woman, who was supposed to be teaching me the joy of receiving. I took my hand out and went home.

I thought about it later and figured people work harder when they're happy. Maybe this was the way I could keep her from being holier-than-thou.

So, the next session I suggested, "If you come first, maybe I'll feel more comfortable."

She looked surprised, then told me what she liked. She added, "I have to rub my clit, and if you make fun of me, you're out the door." We went into the bedroom, and I passed her test. Then she fucked me like a pro. In the middle of it all, I interrupted.

"It feels great physically, but I don't feel anything emotionally, so let's stop." And that was the beginning of me saying what I want.

She had obviously made some changes in the months since I walked out; she was easier to talk to, more vulnerable. I started bringing her dark red carnations instead of pink ones, and she kept giving me advice. She straddled my waist while I was on my back and whispered, "Tell me about your first time." I couldn't think too clearly cuz I could smell her professionally trained and licensed wetness. I just thought about getting my cock in her. But I don't have a cock, so I told her about my first big orgasm with a woman instead. Julie looked down at me.

"Don't have sex with anyone who can't sit with your monsters." Stupid therapist talk, but I loved the way her cunt hair was shaved into a black mohawk.

"Yeah, right, whatever."

"I want you to promise me you won't have sex with people who don't respect you." Her eyes were big and brown, and suddenly I understood why it's important to keep your clothes on around people.

Two days later when Julie my talk therapist was rubbing my back and lecturing me for being so insensitive, I surprised myself, ordering, "Get your hands off my ass and get out of my house!" I haven't seen her since. Not that I want to. I'd rather be hit by a truck.

During the week, sex-surrogate Julie called to tell me to bring my vibrator to our next session since that was my sure fire way to orgasm. Hers was a low-output vintage model. I left mine at home. I had just dreamt about a multi-armed goddess who breast fed me and bestowed the sword of Camelot on me. Something extraordinary was happening. I didn't want to worry about buzzing metal gadgets.

I told her it was more important to me to love someone than to be loved. I didn't know why—that's just the way I felt. She was so smart. She said love had a lot to do with trust. We talked about matters of the heart at the beginning of each session. She asked me lots of questions about what made me feel good and how I had been hurt. She seemed like she had been hurt real bad. I was careful not to ask too much; she was careful not to tell.

I started eating better and dressing sharp. I've always been powerful, but knowing she wasn't going to bring me down, I enjoyed my power. I got hot making her feel good. I could tell she had never been fist-fucked. Both of us were surprised at the resulting crescendo. One day I brought my strap-on and asked if I could fuck her. She said she didn't have intercourse with clients because things going in and out of her were too hard on her. I told her I loved it when she said no because it made yes all the better. Then, I took off my clothes and stood naked and panting in her living room. I've never really thought of myself as sexy, so I loved watching her struggle to maintain professional composure.

During our last session, she first noticed the cherub tattooed on my shoulder, and I first noticed the tiny heart tattooed on her thigh. She said she had something to show me. She said she wanted to end her twenty-nine-year career with a bang, then she lifted her dress. She had totally shaved her cunt. At first I didn't like it, but when she put her legs together, she looked classy, like a well-tucked drag queen.

In bed, I told her my dream, the one I had been waiting all week to tell her. I was at a huge banquet with exquisitely dressed people. They laughed and feasted. I was dressed in my ripped-up, hike-around-town sweat pants and T-shirt. Everybody loved me dearly.

Julie kissed my neck and whispered, "They love you because you're so much yourself."

Both of us twitched when she said that. I wasn't sure what she meant, but when I kissed her, it was soft and hungry. Like kissing someone you're in love with for the very first time. Like kissing girls used to be. No, it was better, because I was falling in love with myself, and I promised to stick around this time.

When the phantoms and fears came, I just breathed deeper and watched them go by. With Julie's fingers deep in my ass and cunt, I came like a skydiver on a free-falling honeymoon.

When you can say no, it makes yes all the better.

Adventures in Dick-sucking, or why I love to suck Butch cock: An oral History

Bree Coven

Okay, I admit it: I love giving blow jobs. I didn't like it with men, in fact, I never did it with men. I learned how to give good head from a very hot, very butch, dick-wielding lesbian. I was twenty at the time, living a happily lesbian-feminist-separatist existence, snug in my non-role-playing p.c. academic world. I think I hated men as much as I loved women. I was *repulsed* at the thought, mention or sight of a penis. Then, one day, making gentle, tender, PG-13 love with my sweetie, she stopped me and said, "I'm sorry, I just can't do this." I sat up, shocked. "What? What did I do wrong?" She shook her head. "No, it's not that. It's not you. I just can't do this soft and sweet 'I'll go down on you, you go down on me' thing. I don't want you to lick my pussy." My face fell. I was bewildered. Until she finished her sentence: "I want you to suck my dick."

Okay, so I was only twenty, and out a mere three years. I'd only had sex with one woman before her, my college roommate, and our sex was very egalitarian and vanilla. We were so innocent, we naively used dental dams every time even though neither of us had ever had any kind of sex with anyone else ever. We'd heard about lesbians getting AIDS, so we were careful and dutifully devoted to our latex. If we didn't have it, couldn't get it, we didn't have sex. Period. We laugh about this now, only wishing our dedication to safer sex had followed us into our older, more promiscuous years. So my knowledge of lesbian sex was pretty slim. I'd never seen a porno. I'd never heard of a dildo. I thought B&D meant Black and Decker. And I was puzzled as to how this new, older, wiser and more experienced lover wanted me to suck her "dick" when it was clear she didn't have one. I was, nevertheless, intrigued.

"Um, you want me to what? But..." She shushed me. "Honey, do you know what I'm thinking when you put your sweet lips on me?" I didn't. "I'm thinking of how I want them wrapped around my dick. I'm picturing my clit, hard and extended into a lesbian cock, hot and engorged for you, and I'm picturing you wanting me and taking me into your sweet little mouth." My eyes about popped out of my head. But I was eager to please. So she reached under the bed, pulled out a small red velvet bag and ordered me to close my eyes, and when I reopened, there she was with a proud set of balls and an eight-inch dick strapped to her pelvis.

We began my lessons that evening. I found that, from my first taste, I *loved* that dick. I was a natural, pulling her into my throat, sucking her skin against the roof of my mouth, running my tongue along the length of her. I have a big mouth for a little girl, and I nearly wet myself the first time I was able to take all of her, swallow her whole, and hold on to her ass while she buried that dick in my face. I liked feeling the length of her stiffness disappear into my mouth, and letting my tongue play at the ridges, while my nails raked the underside of her balls, then, lightly, flicking my tongue catlike at the head, barely tasting her, tickling the tip until she could no longer stand my teasing and grabbed the back of my head, forcing herself down my throat, jamming her cock, hot and swollen, into my face, fucking me full-force until I was so full of her I thought I would cry. I became an avid dicksucker that summer. I loved my newfound way of pleasing my lover, on her terms. My physical acceptance of her cock was my way of embracing her butchness, of surrendering to her will. I never licked her clit again after that. It was me and the dick—anytime, anywhere she wished. We'd go out to dinner and she'd be packing the smaller one, and I'd make a game of rubbing the ball of my foot against her under the table. I would cup her hardness in the cab on the way home and she'd struggle to keep a straight face as I went down, right there in the back seat, the knees of my stockings getting dirty as I knelt before her, smearing my lipstick on her pants, then deepthroating her butchness, taking as much of her into my body as I possibly could, wanting her dick, her desire to completely engulf me. When we got home, she'd relax before the television, legs spread, in the silk boxers I'd bought her, her dick poking through the fold in the fabric and I would have to stop whatever I was doing and go to her and try to get her attention, by kneeling at her feet, massaging them, then working my way up to her hard-muscled thighs and finally playing with her cock as it stood there, at attention. I would roll her hardness between my hands before taking her into my mouth and she would play games with me, looking over the top of my head at the television, but getting gradually more distracted by my grunts of pleasure as I noisily sucked at her, allowing her rubber to slap against my lips and the roof of my mouth. Once I got really into it, my whole head bobbing up and down on her rigidness, frantically fucking her with my face, she would have to take note, and though the TV would still be on, the program was abandoned, as we fell to the floor, her grunting and thrusting her hips towards my face to give me more, more, as I let her feel my teeth and sucked her as hard as she had fucked me the night before. She grabbed a fistful of long disheveled hair and held my head still as she had her way with me; I kept my lips in a perfect tight O as she rocked back and forth and then slammed her body into me full-force, coming hard into my mouth. I sat still, holding her in my mouth, cradling her dick between my lips until she quieted down and gently pulled me up onto her chest, which heaved under her ribbed tank top. Her dick was strong and beautiful and possessed us both with a force that can barely be put into words. I just know that I have never felt so power-ful, so sexy, or so very femme as when I am before a lover on my knees, taking her into my mouth and giving her all I have to offer.

Don't get me wrong: I love getting fucked—fingers, dildos, fists—but nothing beats the exchange of power when I am sucking my butch off. I give a good blow job, and I love it, and I love the way it makes my butch feel. I can tell, because in addition to "sweetheart" and "honey" she calls me "the best little cocksucker in the world"—a title I am proud of as it is my way of giving back the love my butches have so freely lavished on me.

Lay Lady Lay

Red Jordan Arobateau

Truck is warm. Night outside. Rustle of bushes in the wind.

Arm around her, Whitey pulls Nicki close. Fingers touching inside her wet chamber. She was big. Soft, wet. Ran her fingers in and out, banged the palm of her hand against the woman's clit. Still heard no response. *Well, she'll show me.*

Kept on. *She'll show me what she wants in body language. It must be okay. Ain't got no complaints from the ladies yet.*

Whitey's clothes were pushed over the side, by the arc of the metal truck. Her belt ran through the loops of worn blue jeans, knife in the sheath. Solid metal, glistening sharp.

* * *

It was so good, and it had been such a long time—a woman wanting her. Smile came to Whitey. She knew she was going to bust a nut if her clit came in contact with any part of the woman's body. Enjoyed the sensation. Wondered, *When is she going to get hot? Ain't heard a sound yet, or felt much motion. Wonder how she likes to cum.* So then Whitey couldn't stand it, took her fingers out of her cunt, raised her body up on her hands, looks down at Nicki into her blue eyes.

"What do you like me to do best little lady?"

"Just go for it honey. Go ahead." And slaps Whitey's ass.

The butch craved to put her cunt on the femme's blond cunt.

Crickets chirp. Waves. And Whitey crawled between her legs, by pressure of her body opens the woman's thighs, rose up, her tits dangle over her, white belly flat. As her cunt moved onto Nicki's, hot currents of pleasure passed through her body. Began moving her hips.

Woman spread her legs right away, and held her knees back with her hands, so the butch got right in there. Panting, sweat drips off of her. Looks down, sees fine blond hair. The bed is rocking with her thrusts. Her cunt rides around on Nicki's, working for a climax. Wets two fingers in spit and reaches down, pulls her pussy lips open to get her clit fully up against her cunt. Knees on the mattress, hands hold her upper body up; the woman's legs in the air, cunt buried in cunt. Hips go round and round, up and down, riding her, cunt juices mingling. Hot desire burned fire below, increasing as the tempo increased. Fire grew in her belly, in her throat, in her sex. Hot. Waves of pleasure rolled over and over.

* * *

It all came back now—real lovemaking, asking a partner what she wanted. The motion, the rhythm of their two bodies. The Lady knew how to do it, do it good. Mutual enjoyment, after absence of nearly a year; of one-sided sex for her own gratification; quickie cum in one night stands with sleazoids; and a "pay lady" for hire out of a massage parlor in a back street of the Tenderloin.

Thrust her hips, drove her sex into the woman's between her spread thighs; delicious feeling swept over her. Clang! Clang! Knife hit the metal walls.

The truck. On her back waiting for the butch to finish with her, the woman looked around. *It's like a fortress.* And she felt held. Dyke on top of her moving, groaning, gave her a glow between her legs, and brought her back to a state of feeling once more, from a long numbness of no feeling. Heard a voice speak.

"Is it in the right place honey?"

"Feels good."

Felt the butch's wet pussy against hers. Nicki wiggles her neat little cunt of blond wispy hairs; her juicy, wet thighs on the mattress. Whitey goes to town. Thrusts her hips back and forth, inhales short breaths. One hand squeezes Nicki's tit.

Breathless, "Are you gonna cum?"

"Go ahead baby." Soft voice came from a distance.

"OHHHHHHHHHHHHH!! AHHHH!!" Raises up on her hands, one on each side of her on the bed. Got ready to climax.

"OHH! HUH HUH!" Goes up and down, each thrust drives bolts of sexual pleasure to eat up her desire, gaining release.

All mine, have this for four days.

"OH SHIT! UH HUHH!"

And the woman waited, humped under her; caressed her sweaty back, waiting until Whitey was through. And Whitey thinks, *Maybe she just lets me screw her because I brought her up here and she don't really want it...Shit.*

As Whitey moved her clit around in a little circle in Nicki's cunt she knew. *I'm conquering the world.* "Are yuh gonna cum baby?"

"Maybe," the woman breathed.

"OHH IT'S SO GOOD BABY!"

"So I've been told."

Her cunt in the woman's, up and down, round and round; beneath her, humping; palms of her hand push Whitey's ass into her. Jacking off her clit against the woman's cunt.

Deep throbbing currents continue, head to toe. Leans down, kissing and panting. *Didn't work quite right. She didn't cum. What does she want me to do for her?*

* * *

So, she had done what'd she cum to do. And done what she could. Whitey wondered, *What does this filly want me to do for her?* Whitey had ridden her, sucked her, finger fucked her...Well, that left the dildo.

So, silent, strong Whitey held Nicki in her arms, stars outside in the night, felt her own heartbeat slow back to normal after her climax.

Knowing the woman would tell her in body language as she stroked between her legs, fingers delving into the ripe cunt; now going into her was ex, soft empty cavity of her vagina. Tried to put three fingers in.

The woman sighed, "It's okay."

Worked them around in her wet cavity, head bent, kissing, sucked her tits. Sound of fingers coming in, out of her, wet slap, slap.

The woman felt a low grade of sensuality build; the need in her cunt, up inside her vagina, in her tits, her throat; all erogenous zones, as Whitey loved her. Her hips stirred. Loving her. Wanting to be taken until the hunger stopped.

Whitey's strong fingers inside her cunt.

"Harder, do it harder." The woman moaned.

Rubbed Nicki's clit with the palm of her hand while she penetrated her cunt with three fingers and then she had her tongue in Nicki's mouth simultaneously.

Whitey waited to hear her women make noise, holler, moan, so she knew she was doing something to them—but only breathing at an increased rate came from this lady who lay in her arms.

"Put four fingers in me."

So, still working it, palm of her hand on her clit; so big inside, had felt waves of her vagina, but barely feels the walls anymore.

"Let me get the vibrator."

"I don't need it, unless you want to."

Whitey stopped. Woman lay back.

"Now little lady," Whitey spoke in a sonorous tone. "I got these toys under the mattress." Nods her head in that direction. "Don't be embarrassed. I even got one that vibrates. I got this dick. It don't get soft. I can give it to you all night long. And give it to you any way you want."

Went under the mattress by the metal arc of the truck, comes out with the dildo. Rubbery plastic bendable and dependable. Showed it to her.

"It's eight inches."

Took it by the base, slapped it into her hand. "I'll make it good to you."

"If you want to," Nicki says, but don't look like she cares.

"I can give you more than any man can give you baby. I'll take my time and give you everything you need. I'm not finished just 'cause I cum. I'll give it to you all night." She put the tool down, got its belt-like harness strapped around her hips. The cock stuck out of her pubic mound. Fastened two buckles, one on each side. Whitey knew in no time Nicki's cunt would be swollen with passion. Got the KY jelly; lube drops from the tube.

Goes between her legs, on her knees; pushed the woman's knees up; cock strapped between her legs, and went into her. And they began rolling around.

The woman was as if a spectator; watching herself from a long way up. Saw flickering candlelight make dancing shadows. The metal ceiling four feet above their heads; and Whitey's long blond hair on her, body sweating, slipping, as she hung on.... Heard sounds of her cunt being fucked, slow and forceful, then faster; slap wet. Incense burning. Time went by. The base of the cock buried in Whitey's pubic mound as it goes in then out. And Whitey fiddled with the nipples on her tits like knobs. A vague excitement grew.

"Harder baby, harder. It's okay, you won't hurt me, I can take it."

Maybe she likes a little pain. Hand reached up, pulled the woman's arm down and held it. Felt Nicki twist under her and make a little intake of twisted her arm.

"That's good," the woman said, "Hurt me."

So Whitey kept on. The murky waters started to come clear.

Whitey was excited. The base of the cock banged against her clit.

Sound of fucking and grunts, of efforts Whitey made. Music of love. Nicki, passive, lay in her arms, so light, like a cloud.

I've held women down before, Whitey thought. So, took the woman's arm, twisted it under her, had a hammer lock. The woman seemed to respond, pinned to the mattress, wrestling her, strong, and the woman's legs spread eagle.

"I want it baby! I want your cunt!" Whitey grunts. Talking dirty to excite her. "I want you! I'm putting my hard cock in you baby! I'm doing it to you! Do you feel my hard cock inside you? Is it good? Do you feel it? Take it all the way! Take it!"

Thrust it in, drew it out, teased near the opening then pushed it in. Brought it out, not all the way, and reached down between them, roughly rubs the woman's clit, jacking it up and down. Then, "Take my hard cock baby."

Her hand put it back in Nicki, hips plunged to the hilt.

"Take it baby."

She came out almost, then thrust it in all the way.

"Feel my hard cock in you, it's just what you need," Whitey said. "You know you want it." Pushed it in and out. "Take it baby. You know you want it.... You know you want it."

She let Whitey do everything to her she desired. Now lay back and took it. The butch notes, *She ain't righteously getting into this. Ain't making no noise...I've got to do a good job of this!*

* * *

"Alright little lady. How can I turn you on?" A wiser Whitey asked. Warm, willing.

"Well..." a little voice answered.

penetration

CECILIA TAN

You think I'm going to tie you down and fuck you, don't you. You think I'm going to strap on a dildo, and do this intercourse thing, play butch boy for you, and let you scream and carry on, indulge your rape fantasies and all that good stuff, that stuff that gets you so hot, that makes you drip wet.... I can see you dripping now, from the way I grabbed you by the hair and forced you into the bonds, spread eagled on your bed. Maybe it's the bed, especially, that makes you think we're going to fuck, and maybe it's all the hints you've been dropping me about the way you like it, the things you've done...you're a smooth bottom, practiced, you've been with badder bitches and butches than me. So if I'm going to give you what you want, I know, I've got to give you something you don't know you want. I'm going to start with my finger. I pull off my leather glove and toss it away, and work my index finger right between your wet lips, right into the hot spot, and into you it goes. I can see the look in your eyes—what, no foreplay? no clit action?—but as my finger slides as deep as it can go, your eyes close and you gasp with deep pleasure. Then two fingers. You don't need foreplay, you don't need lube, sweet thing, your cunt is hungry and I'm going to feed it. Next, I pull a dagger from my pocket. It's not a dagger, it's a letter opener, but you don't know that. I see you gasp and flinch and squirm—you think I'm going to pretend to cut you, run the tip all over your flesh, across your nipples.... I see your eyes go wide as I dip it between your legs. Have you figured it out yet? I slide the dull metal into you, using the flat blade like a tongue depressor, to peer into the folds of your flesh. Your vagina convulses as you realize what I'm doing and you strain against your bonds, helpless to stop me. I know if you really want to stop me you'll say the word. But you're too interested, wondering what I'm going to do next. I pull a magic marker out of my pocket and write my name in flowing script across your belly, then cap the thing and hold you open with the fingers of one hand while I slide the hard plastic cylinder into you. Your legs are shaking as I move it in a wide circle...what are you thinking, darling? Have you ever put a magic marker up your cunt before? Is this something you used to do when you were a kid, under the sheets at night, terrified of being caught, but unable to stop your own lust—what did you turn to when your fingers weren't enough? The marker is not large, but it is hard and foreign, is that what's making you shake? The thought of this thing protruding out of your body, probing into places it was never intended to go? You almost laugh when you see the kielbasa, a thousand phallic puns half-remembered flicker across your face as your eyes take in the curve of sausage in my hand. No, I wouldn't, you think. But I will, and I do, rolling a condom onto the end for full phallic effect and pushing the thickness against your lips until they give way and then inching it inside. You whimper, a sweet sound. It feels big, I know it, I see you clenching and relaxing, trying to take it in—good girl. It's too soft to fuck you with so I settle for burying it a few inches deep and then leaning down to bite off the end. When my nose rubs your clit I stop my nibbling and pull the meat out of you, toss it away. Too late I realize I should have made you eat some of it, should have let you taste your own juice on it. No matter, there is more in store. The unlit end of a burning candle. You twitch as you feel the heat of the flame although I'm the one who gets wax on her hands as I'm moving it from side to side inside you. A pair of black lacquer chopsticks, so thin you barely feel them at all, until I split them like a speculum and widen you side to side, top to bottom. I let you lick them when I'm done. What else can we stick into your cunt, my girl? I've used up the things that I brought with me, so I cast about your apartment looking for more. You've got dildos galore but they don't interest me, cunt girl. I roll a condom over an Idaho potato I find in your fridge, cold and fat and wide, and I push the tip of it in as far as it will go. I fuck you with it until it is sliding in up to its widest point, and you are moaning and thrashing. Have you ever been fucked with something this big, cunt girl? You probably have, I don't kid myself after all the hints you gave me. Have you ever slept with a man? The potato is getting slick and hard to hold onto, but I'm shoving it with my palm into you now. I bet you have slept with men, before, even if you haven't said anything about it to me. How could that hungry cunt resist? A pole of hard, hot flesh, that fits snug and twitches in response. I'd love to have one, myself, love to have one to ram into you and feel your wetness on every nerve ending. But there's no use wishing for things I don't have, and what I have is you, wide open before me, your cunt is my cunt and I can put anything into it that I like. The potato slips out onto the floor and your head jerks up, your vagina gasping like a fish, so empty, so needy. A bottle of shampoo. The handle of a hairbrush. Pinking shears. Yours is the cunt that ate Tokyo. When I'm done with you there won't be a phallic object left in your apartment that doesn't smell like your desire. Everything will remind you of me. I am just beginning to wish I had a crusty baguette to go with the kielbasa when I decide maybe you've had enough. You sense the hesitation and look up, hope in your eyes. No, I'm still not going to fuck you. You realize it when I pack the harness back into my bag. You want to ask so bad, I see you holding back, you want to beg me for something but you aren't sure whether you can abase yourself that way. Silly girl, you'll let me stick anything into your slit as long as you're tied up. Maybe next time, I'll sit and watch while I order you to stick things up into yourself: a flashlight, a fake rubber dog bone, the old standby: a cucumber. Maybe I'll take photographs of each of these things sticking out of your cunt to horrify my politically correct friends. You're biting your lip with impatience—I'm sorry, my sweet. I get this way sometimes. For now, what kind of a top do you think I am? Don't worry, I'll get you off. After all, I've brought a whole array of things to try on your clitoris: fur, sandpaper, chains, a nail file, macramé rope, a hairbrush, a braided thong, and when I run out of those I'm sure there are more things here I can try. I'm not tired, not in the least.

flying dreams
RAVEN B. KALDERA

Deseret awoke with her heart pounding, a scream nearly escaping her lips. It took a few disoriented seconds to make out the plain beige walls of the dormitory room, to hear the even breathing of her roommates in their beds. She sat up, wrapping the blankets around her thin legs and shivering in spite of the too-warm room. Everything was too warm on CYU; the climate control was always set at a higher temperature than she was used to at home. Most of the students were Earthers, "hothouse Earth" as Janine in her geo class joked, and were used to higher temperatures. Deseret deliberately slowed her breathing and waited for the derms in her temple underwear to turn on a mild sedative. When it didn't come, she realized why with a sinking heart. She'd had nightmares every night for a week now; the garment was programmed to consider this the sign of a guilty conscience and was withholding sedative in order that she might pray and discover the source of her nightmares.

She sat forlornly with her head on her drawn-up knees for a few minutes longer, hoping to stall the inevitable, and then, sighing, got up with the blanket still wrapped around her and knelt beside her bed. As she fought to keep her breathing slow and even in order to reach the proper state, her lips moved soundlessly in the opening prayers. By the time she got through them, the nightmare was like a vague image in the distance, something about pain and longing and billowing curtains of scarlet and purple, like a runny watercolor in all the shades of blood. Was it a bad omen? She couldn't remember enough of it to tell. *Please, O Lord, deliver me from this evil,* she prayed desperately. *Deliver me from the impurity in my mind, from the sin in my soul.*

After an hour of kneeling on the hard floor until her legs ached, she slipped back into bed, exhausted enough not to need the sedative. *I had better get over this before the Elder notices the readings my temple garment is giving out and sends me back home for help;* she clutched the sheets around her in dismay at the thought. So few Adamians ever left their asteroids, and very few girls on Adam-Ondi-Amen were chosen for the honor of going to CYU. With a degree, she could help her people at home by learning to upgrade the failing systems and life-support, the increasingly infertile hydroponics. "It was a mission of life or death," Elder Graves had told the young students as they sat in a taut, excited row, all dressed alike in their white jumpsuits. "We all depend on you."

I hope I won't be too tired tomorrow in hermeneutics class, she thought sleepily as her eyes sank shut. She had been bleary-eyed in too many classes lately. She was left though with the nagging feeling that her praying tonight had been in vain, at best only an aid to exhaustion. She had not been able to bring herself to actually think about the catalyst that had started the nightmares, had not been able to speak the name of the presence she wanted—and did not want—to purge. Now, on the very edge of sleep, she said it twice. "Neidra," she whispered. "Neidra."

* * *

"Bhaktipan women always smile like this," Neidra laughed, and struck a pose with glassy eyes and a curved, blasé Mona Lisa smile of patience. "As if they're all really saying, 'Why do I have to put up with this asshole I'm married to?' Look at all the pictures, even from Earth India thousands of years ago. You'll see that same smile." The dark almond eyes in her perfect, heart-shaped, olive-skinned face twinkled, and her smile morphed into a mischievous grin. She wasn't smiling at Deseret, wasn't even looking at her; Neidra's attention was on the half-dozen other students crowded around her, and Deseret was actually glad of that. Not only because Adamians had strict orders not to fraternize with the other students, except to witness to them. Her heart was pounding and her palms damp from just being five feet away.

Then leave, she tried to tell herself sternly, but her feet somehow refused to move. She kept watching Neidra, her slightly plump, full-breasted figure, her delicate tiny hands adorned with multiple bracelets, the great cloud of fluffy black hair to her waist. What must it be like to touch that hair, to brush it smooth? It must be coarser than her own limp, mousy hair, but much thicker. *It wouldn't be a sin to enjoy the feeling of brushing Neidra's hair,* she pleaded with herself. It would be just like sisters, the sister she never had. Wouldn't it?

Danila was talking now, recounting some event in her Politics of Gender class. *His,* Deseret reminded herself fiercely. No matter how pretty and feminine Danila might look, he was a spawn of Satan, a walking sin. He had been born male, and no body change could alter that, according to Adamian doctrine. If Deseret could name a single thing that had horrified her the most, the greatest source of culture shock upon coming to CY University, it would have to be the nachtlei from Karanda, the third-gender people with their special names for themselves, their bright, flamboyant clothing and their utter lack of sexual prudery. Not just the androgynous ones, who you couldn't tell what they were. She was completely unnerved, instead, by the ones who looked perfectly normal but had once been something else. She couldn't even bring herself to look Danila in the eye.

She noticed one thing about Danila, though. Her hands. Large, beringed hands with long glittery nails. Too big for a woman's, but not like a man's. And one of them was slipping gently, flirtatiously, into Neidra's tiny brown one.

Deseret turned away from the group, hugging her bookpad to her, and went down the hall, sick to her stomach. She tried to tell herself that her overwhelming feeling of wrongness was horror at the idea of that perverted creature touching anyone, especially sweet, laughing Neidra. But the more she examined the emotion from the corner of her eye, the more she realized that it was just seething jealousy, plain and simple. The realization made her even sicker.

Her roommate Emma caught up with her at the end of the hall. "I have bad news," she whispered. "Elder Nephi is going to speak to you on Friday, before services. I heard him talking over the com while I was downloading the morning prayers onto the pads. Something about your monitoring. What did you do?" At Deseret's frightened white face, she glanced around and continued in a falsely compassionate tone, "You can tell me. It's all right. We're friends, remember?"

"I—I don't know," Deseret stammered. "I haven't done anything. I go to class, I..." She trailed off. Could the temple underwear that she had been sealed into at the age of twelve, impregnated with its monitors to check her heart rate and blood pressure and general health, to help her sleep and ensure no mind-altering substances went into her blood, could it have sensed something? And what?

One thing was sure. As of Friday, she was doomed.

* * *

"Feels nice, dear, doesn't it? Neidra's very good at her job." Professor Chemarin stroked Danila's hair as Neidra's tiny but capable hands dug into her back, banishing the sharp crystalline knots of lactic acid. Prostrate on the neosilk bedsheets, Danila could only moan with pleasure, a sleepy smile on her face.

"This won't affect my grades, will it?" she mumbled from the depths of the pillow. Danila knew there was something in the CYU rules that probably disapproved of ending up in a threesome with a classmate and your parapsych prof, but she had had a crush on both pretty Neidra and the tall, brilliant, chocolate-skinned professor since coming here. It was like a dream come true, especially for a nachtlei like herself, who found it hard enough to get lovers. Neidra finished the massage and began to kiss the back of her neck, kisses moving slowly down her spine until her tongue flicked into the crack of Danila's ass, making her forget all about grades. Neidra laughed softly and her tongue flicked deeper, worming its way into Danila's asshole. The nachtlei girl moaned and thrust her ass up, letting Neidra wrap her arms around her hips. She was vaguely aware of Professor Chemarin ("Call me Bess," the older woman had said, but Danila was too intimidated) brushing the hair away from the back of her neck, setting her mouth to it in a teasing kiss.

"So you've been having dreams, have you?" came the smooth voice in her ear. Neidra had her up on her knees now, and she could feel that hot mouth moving down to her genitals. Although it was impossible to concentrate on what the Professor was saying, Danila heard something similar to "I can show you what they mean. Just relax and let go."

The older woman had her by the hair now, in what seemed to be an iron grip, turning her head to the side. She caught a glimpse of one dark purple-tipped breast showing through the neosilk kimono, and then that full mouth was on her neck again. She was suddenly painfully aware of the lines of energy running through her body like currents, like golden rivers flowing in and out. Mostly flowing downward now, toward the place where Neidra, now on her back with her head between Danila's thighs, was coaxing such pleasure out of her.

Then Professor Chemarin got her teeth into the muscle of Danila's neck and sucked.

It was agony and ecstasy. The streams of golden energy were forcibly pulled upwards, rushing from her groin to her throat and...outwards? The oral sex went on and on, and she was kept at the very edge of orgasm, unable to come, until that cruel mouth released her throat and she swooned into an orgasm fiercer than anything she had ever experienced. She seemed to be at once in herself and Neidra, to feel both her own peak of pleasure and Neidra's wet hunger and elation at having made Danila buck and thrust like an animal in rut. And there was more...stars, planets, circling mounds of space dust, a thousand minds of the population of CYU, some open to her and some not. The Professor was a curious blankness in all of this, a place barred to her. As the sensations faded, Danila curled up into herself, wondering, with her head in Professor Chemarin's lap, a safe haven, a breathing space, a place where she could think her own thoughts and no one, no one would intrude upon them ever again.

Danila felt Neidra's warmth against her back. "You'll be all right," she whispered. "It was a little weird for me too at first, being fed on. But pretty soon you'll have everything under control." And she spoke the Word that no one else but Danila could know, a word that had no meaning and yet meant everything—safety and love and an outpouring of acceptance—a word that had been with her as long as she could remember, that had sustained her through her change.

"How did you know about that?" the nachtlei whispered.

"It's simple." The Professor's rich accented voice sounded above them, as if from a far distance. "I met both of you long ago, when you were children. You and many more. You were special, gifted. I gave you that Word, and it brought you here. To join the Dream."

"The Dream?" Danila was ready to believe anything at that moment, even this.

Neidra laughed. "I'll show you," she said, and pressed her fingertips against Danila's temples.

* * *

"It's hardly my fault. I couldn't have reckoned on those horrible suits they wear." An antique letter opener shaped like a sword was stabbed viciously into the resin desktop through a pile of test papers. It stayed upright, like a cross-shaped grave marker. "They hadn't started using the awful things when I was last there."

"When was that?" asked the visitor, a nondescript man who no one would ever notice in a crowd, or be able to recall if they saw him alone. There was something almost unnerving about his anonymity. "A dozen years ago? You've had time to check the new Adamian practices and make allowances for the suits, and the dermal hormone blockers."

"You don't understand" came the sharp, decisive voice. "Those dreams are keyed into the sexual responses. That's how we reroute the awakening energy, so it doesn't come out in...other ways."

"Like the girl who set her window curtains on fire?"

"Yes, but those were the early days, when the Circle had too many prudes in it. Under my program, we've learned that when you're cracking open a teenager, sexual energy is the best bleed-off.

"Stein, the poor child's libido is repressed entirely by the dermal chemicals in that suit. They all are. Nice and sexless and celibate until they're married off. You know, they aren't even allowed to masturbate. I wonder if AOA Elders are going to start artificial insemination soon so as to remove a need for sex altogether. At any rate, without that outlet, the Aquila Dream comes across as a nightmare. Poor little thing."

"We could give up, send her away," remarked Stein. "Off CYU, she'd be out of range for the Dreams. It'd be easy. They're so paranoid—one remark to her Elder about her performance slipping and she'd be home in a week."

"Where she'll probably go mad. Once you crack 'em, most stay cracked. It's a rare new psi who can get shields up by themselves, and figure out what's going on without help."

"You did," the man acknowledged.

An amused chuckle. "Yes, but we all know what I am, don't we? No, this girl is a Sensitive. She'll end up in a padded room, or worse. The only thing I can think of is to have her quietly disappear."

"That's insane! There'd be nothing quiet about it! The Adamians would raise a holy stink the size of a planetoid, and we'd never see another one of their students again. And the investigation...CYU would have our asses."

There was silence for a moment. "There will have to be an accident. That's all I can say." A long-fingered, chocolate-skinned hand gripped the miniature sword hilt until the knuckles turned white. "I have a responsibility to this girl, Stein. I touched her, as a child. I planted the command. I pulled the strings to get her admitted. It's because of me that her life is shattering. She could have lived as happily as possible on that repressed 'roid, headblind until the day she died."

The man rose and shrugged. "Gods be with you, then, Holy Damned One. It's a dangerous game you're playing. We'll all disavow you in a minute if you get caught, though. You know we have to." He sounded sad.

"I know." An equal sadness met his tone. "Someday, when there are enough of us, it will be different. But right now, there's work to do. I have to procure a dead body by Friday."

* * *

Deseret tried to lose herself in her studies as the transport whisked along. *We need transports this quiet on Adam-Ondi-Amen,* she thought to herself. *I couldn't study with their rumbling racket. So much to learn, and I may not be the one to learn it after today.* She wondered, her stomach knotting, what she could possibly say to Elder Nephi that could explain her nightmares. Would begging help, pleading? Not likely. The transport stopped at the dorm row before hers and the last two passengers exited, leaving her alone. It made her feel even more abandoned, somehow. She very nearly got up and left a stop early, but there was no point in delaying the inevitable. Then, like a sudden glimpse of hell, the tram blew up. Flames cascaded down the aisle like a flood of crackling death. Deseret screamed, turned to run, and the floor fell out from beneath her. There was blackness, and impact, and then nothing more for a long time.

* * *

A light at the end of the tunnel—the long darkness that stretched on forever. Sensations rocked her as she stumbled along; pain, heat, trembling. *Am I dead? Am I going to hell?* she wondered. Am I already there? Sometimes the ground beneath her feet was sharp hard rock, sometimes vague sponginess. She kept her eyes fixed on that tiny point of light, the point that never seemed to get any closer.

Then, like magic, there was a presence beside her. Deseret felt rather than saw it, and then she could see her clearly, like a deep pink glow in the darkness. Neidra stood a little way down the tunnel, looking around with a worried expression on her face. "Deseret?" she called. "I know you're here. It's okay, I'm going to help you find the way out, but you have to help me first! Can you hear me? Call out anything, I'll find you!"

I hear you, Deseret wanted to say, wanted to scream, but her throat somehow didn't work. It seemed a desperate effort to get air into her lungs. Finally, as she clutched the painfully rough rock wall for support, she managed to get out a small sound, like the mewl of a lost kitten. She couldn't imagine how Neidra could hear it, but she did. Her eyes focused on the Adamian girl just ahead of her. "Why, there you are! Your light's so dim, I almost missed you completely! Here, take my hand." She held out her slender fingers, and Deseret almost flinched away. *I can't*, she thought wildly. *I'll be...but if I'm dead, it doesn't matter any more. Nothing matters. Is Neidra dead too, or*—"Are you an angel?" she choked out.

The small dark girl laughed like bells chiming. "You poor thing. Come on, I'll get you out of here." The extended hand glowed with rose-colored light; Deseret noticed that the warm glow somehow came from within Neidra, lighting her up from the inside. Afraid to trust, but more afraid to be marooned in this dark place, she reached out hesitantly and was seized.

Instantly they were flying, or were they standing still with the point of light rushing toward them? Suddenly, they were standing on the threshold of a great cavern. Glittering stalactites dripped from the ceiling, and the room was lit by a pulsing glow of magenta, scarlet, wine, purple, all the colors of blood. A crowd of figures danced, whirled, writhed to the pounding beat of strange elusive music that slipped away when you tried to listen to it. Neidra's hand on hers was like an anchor; she clung to it in confusion. There was no question; this was the place of her dreams. Maybe this was hell. Maybe Satan had lured her with evil dreams into committing sins in her mind, and then killed her at the moment that she was most impure. Neidra, at her side, towed her as if she was a weightless fluff of thistledown toward the center of the cavern, where a tight ring of people obstructed the view, all mysteriously glowing from within with shifting colored light.

Deseret panicked and tried to pull away, nearly blind with fear. "Stop!" she shrieked. "Get me out of here! I'm a good girl, a daughter of Ad—" Her cry was muffled as Neidra, with an iron grip, pulled her into her arms and held her tightly.

"There, there, it's all right, no one is going to do you any harm here," she murmured as Deseret struggled weakly and then gave in, limp and sobbing. Her face was buried in the dark cloud of Neidra's hair, and it smelled of spices, pungent curry and sweet coconut, and this was so near to her secret fantasy that her will gave out and she surrendered, limp as a baby, to Neidra's gentle stroking. Her thin body felt as if it was on fire, a growing warmth spreading outward from her groin. It was a completely unfamiliar sensation. *This must be hell; I can feel myself burning. I'll burn up. I'll be consumed in the flames of perdition and suffer endlessly.* Yet the warm pressure of Neidra's naked body against hers was so pleasant that some part of her could not really believe—naked?! Why hadn't she seen it before? Neither of them had any clothing on. Bronze skin glided against pale flesh as if greased, like rivers flowing together...No!

Deseret had never been naked since the age of twelve. *My temple garment—but no, I'm dead, I couldn't bring it with me. I'm damned, damned to burn forever.* Tears gathered in her eyes and she let out a moan, rubbing herself instinctively against Neidra's thigh—anything to ease the torture between her own. And then Neidra's mouth was on hers, her curry-spice tongue invading Deseret's mouth, and nothing else mattered. When the kiss finally ended, Neidra wiped the tears from her cheeks and stroked back her matted mousy hair. "Feel better?" she asked.

Actually, from the waist down, Deseret felt worse. The heat and burning sensation was nearly intolerable, and she felt her organs swelling as if they would rupture. Wetness poured down her thighs, and she was afraid to look, assuming something had burst and it was blood. But her fear was somehow lessened by Neidra's gentleness and presence, and she resigned herself. "If I'm damned," she whispered, "I shall do my best to endure these torments with courage, and maybe I shall eventually be released." Her heart beat faster. "Just—just don't leave me."

The Bhaktipan girl laughed at her, eyes twinkling in the way that had always secretly charmed her. "Poor little Deseret. Still thinking this is hell! Oh, sweetheart, how wrong you are. This is just part of the Aquila Dream. I'll show you." She turned and made for the circle of people again, towing a limp Deseret with her. Pushing between them, she brought the Adamian girl forward to see first a fire that leaped bright orange in the center and then—Deseret stiffened, more sure than ever that this must be hell, and she was witnessing the torments of the damned.

Spread-eagled against a dark shape on the far side of the fire was a young boy, his face contorted in an attitude of what must be suffering. As he turned his head, she recognized him briefly from her zero-g gymnastics class. Another young man stood before him, burnished skin gleaming in the flamelight, laughing as a whiplike coil of energy flew from his fingers, caressing the other boy's body. He flinched and writhed, and cried out, thrusting his pelvis forward. As they came closer, Deseret could see his cock, erect and unafraid, obscenely swollen. His tormentor reached out and stroked it, and he cried out again, humping the grip. The sight almost made her turn away, but somehow her gaze was caught and she watched, mesmerized, as the boy was whipped and stroked by turns until he screamed and spouted white fluid in a graceful arc.

Neidra was behind her, full breasts pressed up against her back, hands roving her body, hot breath coming in pants in her ear. Deseret automatically pushed her hands away when they brushed her breasts; her nipples were as hard as they might be in cold weather, but there was no cold here, only the burning. Neidra tried again, only to have Deseret cover her tiny naked breasts desperately with her arms. Her trust in Neidra warred with the shame she felt. Then the Bhaktipan girl forced the issue and pried Deseret's hands away, her grip terribly strong in this strange land of death. One arm pinned her about the waist, holding them down; the other slim brown hand found first one nipple and then the other, rolling and twisting them between the slender fingers. Her groin felt as if it would explode, and she moaned in terror and ecstasy. Neidra let go of Deseret's arms to press a palm firmly between her legs, and the pressure felt good, a relief to the throbbing swollen sensation. The second her arms were free, though, she folded her arms instinctively over her breasts again, and her thighs clenched on Neidra's hand, unable to stay open.

The darker girl sighed and turned Deseret around to face her, a look of frustration on her face. "You just can't help yourself, can you?" she said, as though she was not expecting an answer. "Oh, well, we have ways of getting around that too." She took Deseret's hand again and towed her toward the far side of the fire, where the dark shape waited.

Terror built in her throat, paralyzing her, blocking any scream she might have made. The shape loomed, and it was a woman, dark as a storm, cloaked in black—or were those wings?—whites of eyes and teeth the only points of light, and yet her out-thrust hands were limned with gold, gleaming like the first morning sun around the blinds. Something moved in the depths of the terrified girl's mind and she cried out, once, "I know you!" and spoke a word, the Word, with sudden utter certainty.

The memory spun within her, fragmented like a broken mirror. A woman, dark as a storm, bending over her child's form, touching her forehead with fingers whose edges glittered golden (or had it all been a trick of the light?) and saying something, laying a traitorous seed deep inside her. The shock held her for one moment, and then those mysterious hands gripped her wrists and she was drawn up, spread out, her body taut and facing the firelight. Her struggles might as well have been against a steel wall.

Something fastened on the side of her throat like a lamprey and then she felt all the fear simply drain away, as if it were being sucked out of her, leaving her weak and still burning. Neidra appeared in front of her and their mouths melded in another long kiss. This time, when her fingers found Deseret's nipples, she was unable to protect herself. Neidra's kisses replaced her hands on Deseret's breasts, moved down her stomach, over her pubic mound. Unseen hands gripped her ankles and dragged them apart as the fluffy dark head buried itself between her labia, licking and sucking. The Adamian girl cried out with the last of her will, and then she was lost in the great flood of sensation that contracted within her again and again. *Perhaps,* came her last conscious thought, *this is the fire that purifies, the flame that will release me.*

* * *

She came to slowly, finding herself lying across a narrow bunk, insulating blankets wrapped around her. A warm body pressed against her through the covers, and Neidra's voice was speaking to someone from what seemed a great distance above her.

"—and we ought to make Aquila by eight tomorrow morning, Standard time, assuming Danila's as good a pilot as she says," the Bhaktipan's merry voice came. "I hope she'll be all right. It'll be a great shock to her."

"You may have to use a sedative if hysteria threatens. I won't be there to eat her fear this time." Deseret wondered lazily who that authoritative female voice distorted by the com belonged to. It sounded awfully familiar somehow. She moved in the warm covers and Neidra noticed her.

"Gotta go, Holy Damned One. I'll keep you posted." Then Neidra was stroking her hair back from her face. "How are you feeling? Are you hungry?"

Deseret struggled to sit up. She was naked, as in the dream—had it been a dream?—but the room was an ordinary ship's bunk, of the kind she had ridden in coming to CYU. And her body felt more real, yet somehow different. "I'm not dead," she whispered. "Not dead."

"No," said Neidra matter-of-factly. "And yes. The person you were is dead. The Adamian Elder was told of your death. Your family has mourned you. Legally, you no longer exist." *But it's all right, you'll do fine.*

The last words were not spoken aloud, and yet Deseret heard them clearly, Neidra's voice echoing in her mind. Her eyes widened and she clutched at the covers. "What! How—"

The darker girl sighed. *Speech is so useless in conveying concepts like this,* she said silently to Deseret. *Look. Listen.* Her fingers brushed the Adamian girl's forehead and a flood of images poured in—people, many people, gifted in strange ways, all hiding, seeking out their kind one by one all over the settled worlds, being spirited away to have their gifts trained because a developing psi mind might be a danger to those around them, might go mad from their proximity. Her dreams— the group dream, the Aquila Dream created by all the psi minds on CYU, existing and yet nowhere, that had sucked her in. Her suit, the temple garment that prevented her from feeling desire—this was revealed to her with a fillip of disgust from Neidra—sliced off by someone's (whose? *You'll find out someday,* Neidra said) capable hands, her hormonal balance normalized, and then the two days of lying semiconscious in Neidra's arms. A lover's arms, being stroked and touched and brought to pleasure again and again, physically and mentally, as the ship sped on its way to—where?

"Aquila," her lover whispered to her. "You'll find out when we get there. I can't explain it to you just yet; your mind can't take too much interfacing until you're stronger."

Deseret sank in a fog of confusion. "Then I can't ever go home again?" she said in a small voice.

"You can go back as soon as it's safe. I promise. You just need some training," Neidra assured her. *And then you'll be a perfect little walking time bomb,* said a strange echo in the air, but Neidra kept on talking and Deseret, shaking her head to clear it, dismissed it as a product of her confusion. "I'll be with you for the first two weeks, the Prof— uh, friends in the system will cover for me at CYU, and by then you ought to be settled in." She snuggled close to the thin Adamian. "Trust me? Please?"

Deseret looked into her brown eyes, sensing that Neidra was withholding mental contact in order not to pressure her, and made her choice. *Even if I do eventually burn in hell,* she thought to herself, *if it looks anything like the Aquila Dream I'll manage.* "Can—can we go back there? To the Dream?"

Neidra sighed and shook her head sadly. "We're out of range here, in space. But we can rejoin it again on Aquila. In the meantime," and her hands were slipping seductively under the blankets to touch Deseret's newly exposed skin, "we'll just have to amuse ourselves in this dimension. We have been, all along, you know; you just don't remember it."

"We have?" Neidra was closed to her and she had no way of telling the truth of this statement.

"We have. You're so sweet and responsive...especially when you're tied up." She lowered her mouth onto Deseret's, and the new psi felt her energy hum in time to the ship's drive as it hurled her off to a new future, painted in all the colors of blood and desire.

Burn
MELISSA KLEIN

The Montague Theater had fallen on hard times. It was a crumbling old palace of a place. Most of its kind had long since sighed their last gasps and succumbed to video stores. But the Montague was still standing, too grand and proud to give in, though its owners had regretfully decided the only way they could continue to show crackly black-and-white classics to grad students and guitar players in the evenings was to show porn films during the day to itinerant winos and businessmen on long late lunches.

The Montague never drew decent crowds on any day of the week, but the closest it came were "Wild Women Wednesdays." This stroke of promotional genius meant that in the afternoons the theater featured "XXX Hot Girl-on-Girl Action!"—exaggerated pussy slurping by buxom blondes (silicone-buxom, Lady Clairol-blond)—while in the evenings the screen was graced by the wise-cracking Mae West or the sultry Marlene Dietrich.

But this Wednesday was thick with wet weather. It would be slow. The streets were slick with oil and rain. I had walked to work hunched over, shivering a little in my thin jacket and short-sleeved shirt, wishing I had worn any shoes but my stupid high-heeled go-go boots. I couldn't help it, though. If Crawley, the sallow, pock-faced manager, was going to force me to wear a white button-down shirt, black skirt and bow-tie, I had to break free somehow. There were only two ways to go in that get-up—French maid or lady cello player. For some perverse reason, I preferred the former, so I came to work in a short black skirt and high black boots.

Crawley seemed to get a kick out of taking the tickets from the business-suited men and watching them walk past me, some pausing to leer like I was part of the show, others scuttling by, embarrassed to admit even to themselves that they were there for a quick jerk-off. Me, I just called it my concession to fashion. This being a little joke on the fact that my job was working the concession stand. Not that you'd ever know it. No one ever actually bought any popcorn during the day shift. I just stood there listening to the horrible seventies' music and heavy panting and squealing of the soundtrack. Sometimes, in spite of myself, I felt a liquid warmth spread from my belly downwards. Animal reaction to animal noises. Today, because of the battering rain, I wouldn't be able to hear much.

I was the one that had suggested investing in a coffee machine for the concession stand. Now in the evening, coffee was consumed fairly regularly by young hipsters, and in the daytime it was consumed fairly regularly by me. Today I had come in shivering, raised my eyebrows in the direction of the ticket booth—the closest I could come to saying hello to Crawley—and started a pot of coffee brewing. I hung my damp jacket in the utility closet. A few bedraggled customers straggled in as I straightened up the concession area and swept the once-plush red carpet of the lobby. These meager duties done, I was lounging against the glass of the lobby doors, appreciating the warmth seeping through the paper coffee cup in my hands, when I saw Danny's motorcycle pull up. Danny. My crazy girlfriend. Shit, she was something else alright. Who else but this big brazen woman would be bold enough to ride her motorcycle out on a day like this to come visit me amidst porn flicks, suits, drunks and junkies?

Danny pulled her bike expertly into place and turned off the engine. She was wearing a leather jacket and worn black jeans, her usual uniform. I watched her strong fingers tug at the straps of her helmet. Watching her fingers gave me that old familiar ache between my legs, made me think of her fingers inside me, of her fingers tightening straps to bind me, hold me down. As she lifted the helmet carefully from her head, she glanced at me, caught me watching her from behind the rain-fogged glass of the doors. She smiled slightly but her heavy-lidded eyes gave away nothing. Her face shone like copper in the rain.

I thought about the time before we knew each other, all the nights I had seen her glide through the pulsing sweat of the one dyke dance club in town, a half head taller than the rest of the crowd. She never danced, just leaned against the bar exchanging low confidences with the bartender, Marie, smoking and drinking what looked like bourbon straight, which Marie poured her for free. How many girls in tight miniskirts took their turns ambling disingenuously over to the bar to clamber up on the stool next to Danny's, turning to her to flirt and flutter their eyelashes? Sometimes Danny took one of these girls home to teach her a thing or two, to treat her good and mean and leave her back at the bar where she had found her. Until the day she took me home. I never left.

"Leslie! Are you going to drink coffee all day and moon around, or are you going to do some work around here?"

Crawley. I sighed.

"What do you need me to do?"

"Well, you could wipe down that glass on the candy counter. There are fingerprints all over it. Then you could clean the ladies' restroom."

A whole theater that smelled like cum and he was worried about a few fingerprints. I dug around for a bottle of 409 and a dirty old rag. I began swiping the rag unenthusiastically along the counter, all the while watching Danny lock up her bike. I loved to watch her do this—her dreadlocks falling in her face, her brown forehead furrowed in concentration, the taut denim of her jeans straining against her broad ass as she squatted to loop the lock through the wheel.

Sam, the projectionist, had started the movie, and Crawley went back into the office. Danny pushed the door open and strode slowly over to the concession stand. She folded her arms on the glass I had just wiped and leaned towards me, smirking.

"Nice outfit, Leslie."

"Are you here to see me or the movie?"

"Maybe a little of both."

There was something intriguing, even arousing, about this idea. Danny, stone-faced, sarcastic Danny, sitting with her arms crossed and engineer boots slung on the seat in front of her, alone and unafraid while around her guys snored or furiously, covertly rubbed their cocks.

"Are you busy?" she asked.

"Well, I have to clean the women's bathroom," I said. "You can come up and talk to me while I do that if you want. Maybe you should go up first so it doesn't look like I'm hanging out with you." I saw her start to reach for the pack of Marlboros in her jacket pocket. "But don't smoke up there. Crawley hates that."

I finished wiping down the counter and walked upstairs to the bathroom, 409 in hand. I actually didn't mind cleaning the bathroom. The

Montague had one of those old-fashioned lounge-bathrooms with red carpet, a couch, high beveled mirrors and dim lamp-light. I could just go there and wipe down the sinks and daydream. And now Danny would be there to keep me company.

I opened the door. Danny was leaning leisurely against the row of sinks. She had draped her leather jacket on the couch and was wearing a white T-shirt. The arms folded across her broad chest were seamlessly smooth with muscle. Behind her head, a window looked out on the parking lot. I could see it was raining in waves, stopping for a moment and then lashing viciously at the window. But this wasn't what caught my attention. What did catch my attention was the cigarette that dangled from Danny's mouth. The cigarette was still unlit, but in Danny's large hand I could see her brass Zippo lighter.

I paused with the door half open, the door whose stern *No Smoking in Restroom* sign was not even graced with a *Please.* I stood looking at her; my jaw had dropped ungracefully open.

"Danny!" I said. "What are you doing? It's not funny, you can't smoke in here!"

Danny shrugged and her thumb flicked at the lighter. A cruel smile played on her mouth, the kind of smile she wore when she meant business, when she went into battle. The kind of smile that at home or at a bar could make the place between my thighs suddenly molten wet. Usually I enjoyed doing battle with her. But now I was angry. What the hell did she think she was doing? She was going to get me fired.

"Danny, someone will see you!"

"Close the door then," she said.

If Creepy Crawley walked by and saw me standing there goofing off and her with a cigarette, that would be it. I let the door close behind me, set the 409 down, and stood with my hands on my hips. The way the widening of her smile coincided with the soft thud of the door closing, I knew I'd made a mistake. She flicked the lighter on, lit the cigarette and took a long drag.

"Danny," I said, trying not to panic, trying to level my voice from pleading to demanding, "you're really going to get me in trouble with the manager. Please, please put out the cigarette and let's open the window."

Danny just looked at me for a moment, the same maddening sardonic smile on her face. She took another drag and tapped ash onto the pristine porcelain of the sink. Then all of a sudden she clamped the cigarette between her lips and turned to heave open the window.

I watched the muscles of her shoulders and back slide like small rolling boulders beneath the T-shirt. The dark old wood frame gave a creaky protesting moan as she forced it. It wouldn't budge further than a foot or so open. I was still standing there, caught off guard by her apparent compliance, when she collared me. I should have been prepared, but I was never prepared for Danny. In one lithe movement she had grabbed me by the neck and dragged me to the window. She forced my head out, and steadied her solid weight in back of me.

"You don't like to smell the smoke?" she crooned, in a mocking infant voice. "Smoke is bad for the little baby girl? I'll tell you what," she said, her voice becoming harsh and husky again, "Daddy's going to make it all better. Daddy's opened the window and Daddy's going to put out her cigarette. But there's not an ashtray here so guess where Daddy's going to put it out?"

God, did she mean me? In all our games, she had never done that. Furious, I writhed against her, trying to pull myself back inside, but she held me fast, her hand clenching a twisted fistful of white uniform shirt and bow-tie collar at the nape of my neck. Her grasp made me feel like a kitten drooping helplessly from its mother's jaws. Angry choked sounds came from my throat. She held me struggling, half-in, half-out of the window. Cold rain hit the back of my head, dampening my dark curls and stroking mocking fingers down my cheeks. I was really angry with her—not the play-anger of sex, but a blinding gnashing anger at my own lack of control. Yet against my will, I was becoming aroused. Habit made my body obey her. The way my pussy mashed against her leg as I bucked was turning me on. Gradually I relaxed a little and settled myself momentarily against Danny's heavy denim thigh. Beneath my panties I could feel the hard muscles of her leg through her jeans. As she sensed the fight in me waning, she released me very slightly, enough at least so that I could breathe and speak.

"Danny," I whimpered miserably, "Please, let me go."

She paused, and though I couldn't see behind me I could hear the concentrated intake of breath as she took a drag on the cigarette and then expelled the smoke from her lungs. That done, she said, "Pull down your panties."

"Danny, I can't! Not here!"

"Pull them down," she said, with infinite patience.

"What if someone comes in?"

"Pull down your panties," she said grimly, enunciating each word from between gritted teeth.

Slowly, I reached back and hitched up my skirt. Slowly, my hands slid down and peeled the satiny elastic from my skin, letting the panties fall from my thighs to the place where my high boots clasped my calves. I could feel the cool damp air from the window raise tiny chill bumps on my ass. I wondered if Danny could see the tell-tale glistening of my pussy. My chest pressed painfully against the ledge of the window and I felt my heart beating fast with desire and with fear—of what she would do, of someone coming in and seeing us. What was it about her that made my desire stronger than that fear?

"Raise your ass, like you do when I spank you at home."

Her voice was calm, which made me more afraid of how merciless she could be, but somehow it helped quell my fear of being caught. Danny would take care of me. She was in control, she would make it alright. I was safe with her.

"Now I'm going to let go of you, but first I want you to put both your arms outside and hold onto the ledge. I can trust you to do that, can't I?"

I placed my arms over the ledge according to her orders but refused to answer. The smoke she exhaled drifted out the window to my nose, along with a faint whiff of my own loamy musk. From the window I could barely make out ribbons of rain falling in the half-light of near-dusk, rain denting the cars below, rain illuminated in a halo around the streetlight. I almost smiled, glad Danny couldn't see me. I could picture the exact look she had on her face, the dark raised eyebrows, the skin tight over her part-Cherokee cheekbones, the full mouth turned down, displeased with me.

"I can trust you to behave yourself like a good girl outside of the house, can't I?"

"Yes." I let out a breath and relented.

"Yes who?"

I teetered on the heels of my go-go boots. The rain beat down harder.

"Yes, Daddy," I said.

"Good girl," she said. "Now I want you to touch yourself. I want you to play with your pussy."

I brought my right arm inside the window. My hand was wet from the rain, my finger cold at first when I brought it inside the hot folds of my cunt. I dipped at the entrance of my hole, slickening my finger with my own oiliness. My palm cupped the rough curlicues of my pubic hair while my middle finger lightly circled my throbbing clit.

"That's it, that's it, you little slut," Danny whispered as she traced a slow path over my bare ass with the cigarette, barely far enough away not to burn my cool skin, close enough so that I could feel and fear its heat. I feared it, yet I wanted it. I wanted her to burn me, to leave her mark on me. I wanted to see if I could take it, to see if I was strong enough to take it without flinching. But because I couldn't see the work of her hand behind me, my flesh flinched and quivered as the cigarette neared. I had trouble keeping up the rhythm on my clit but I could feel my lungs swelling and the muscles of my legs tensing as I moved closer and closer to coming.

While her left hand was preoccupied with the cigarette, Danny slid two fingers of her right hand to the edge of my wet, wanting hole, teasing me until a ragged "Please" was torn from my lips.

"Please what?" she crooned.

"Please, fuck me Daddy," I begged.

She rammed her two fingers into me and my cunt swallowed them, contracting around them. I moaned. Unable to hold back any longer, I came, and as my body shuddered in orgasm she pressed the cigarette into the soft flesh of my ass, branding me. The burning, searing pain mingled with the hot flushed waves of my orgasm just as the words "Danny" and "Daddy" mingled on their way out of my throat as I gurgled them over and over. The rain drummed furiously on the back of my head, pouring in rivulets from my drenched hair.

I lay there for a minute, draped over the ledge, my bare half, dry; my clothed half, soaked. Then I felt Danny's firm hands on my shoulders, and tenderly, gently, she pulled me inside, pulled up my panties, and pulled my skirt down over them as if she was getting me ready for school. She turned me around and held me from her at arm's length. Her brown eyes looked into my blue ones for a long moment, and then I pulled away. I stooped to retrieve the cigarette butt from the floor, threw it out into the parking lot, and closed the window.

"I have to go, Danny. Shit, I've been up here all this time and I never cleaned."

"Leslie. Are you mad at me?"

"Yes," I said. Though I wasn't really. I looked at her and smiled a little at her worried expression. "I'd be more mad if I'd gotten caught and fired. You do realize you put my fabulous concession stand career in jeopardy, don't you?"

"I'll make it up to you at home," she said, with a contriteness I didn't buy for a second.

I smoothed my hair back as best I could, hoping its natural darkness would hide the fact that it was sopping. We walked down the worn carpeted stairs together and Danny went out into the rain. No one was in the lobby, and even if Crawley or Sam had seen us, they wouldn't have suspected. As many "hot girl-on-girl action" flicks as they showed at that theater, I don't think any of the guys that worked there believed lesbianism really happened, that it was anything but a *Hustler* construct for their benefit.

I lifted the wooden partition and let myself into the concession area. I fixed myself a club soda in a large cup with a straw. I was thirsty. The tiny bubbles tickled my throat going down.

Crawley came creeping out of the little rat-hole of the theater. Probably beating off in there with the rest of them. He blinked his rodent eyes at me.

"Leslie! I sent you to clean the bathroom half an hour ago. What have you been doing? And why are you all wet? Where the hell have you been?"

I took a long cool swallow of club soda and looked him straight in the eye.

"Cigarette break," I said.

Ariel

CAROL QUEEN

The first time I visited the Black Rose, the Tenderloin bar where things are rarely what they seem, I was with Dave, a bisexual man with a taste for having it all wrapped up in one neat package. At the Rose he could find a beautiful woman, make an arrangement, and when he raised her glittery skirt, find a succulent cock to suck. The tits wouldn't be fake, either, at least no more fake than you find on most porn stars these days, and Dave was happier with the divine androgynes he met at the Rose than he was with anyone else in his life.

"Of course it's hard to find a girlfriend there," he said, "unless you have a lot of money, 'cause most of them are working to save up for their change. I always found it very hard to be lovers with a working girl. I have too much ego."

The first time I went to the Rose, on Dave's arm, the bar was full of larger-than-life women who looked at me suspiciously, and only the ones who knew Dave came up to speak to us. The men in the bar didn't give me a second look. It wasn't that the queens didn't look like women—most of them did—but that I didn't look enough like them. If there was one thing the men at the Rose weren't looking for, it was a woman in jeans with no makeup.

Dave told me sometimes straight couples cruised the Rose together, but not often, so most of the girls who worked out of the bar ignored any potential I might have had to be a real pay-for-play client. I was only looking that night, anyway, and I wasn't sure it was okay for me to do even that. The Black Rose was a mirror world, a deep secret, and the only safe space most of its habitués had. It wasn't set up to welcome tourists, unless they had money to spend.

The second time I visited the Rose, I went alone.

I didn't go there to cruise or to trick, exactly. I think I cabbed in to the Tenderloin because I knew I could get lost there, because in a weird way the Rose was a safe space for me too, a place where I was almost invisible. When the doorman looked askance at me I mentioned Dave's name; that got me in without further hassle. I took a tiny table off to the side, where I could nurse a drink and see the stage. Sometime after ten o'clock the shiny strips of silver Mylar that curtained the back of the stage began to rustle, and seconds later the first of a dozen transsexuals came through to do her act, lip-synching and dancing to thirty years' worth of diva tunes. As I swallowed stinging mouthfuls of a bad martini, I wondered if something about Judy Garland, Tina Turner, Madonna, Aretha Franklin and Annie Lennox could lure boys away from being boys.

It was like a gay drag show, but equally unlike—less campy by far, although some of the performers were so bad they were good. Huge happy girls towered in their high shoes, barely managing to walk. The Thais, Vietnamese and Filipinas—some of the Latinas too—passed flawlessly, smooth-skinned and no taller than me. Dave had told me that the biggest secret was to get on hormones before the end of puberty. Hardly any of them could do this. Some bore scars from inexpert electrolysis.

She approached my miniature table with none of the attitude I'd gotten from the others. She stood over six feet tall in her heels—the girls at the Rose never, ever wore flats—and she was gorgeous in the bigger-than-life way I was still getting used to. Looking up at her I saw legs for miles, crazy with patterned black lace stockings, a short, shiny silver skirt topping them, and a loose, silky black tank top which didn't quite expose her breasts but showed cleavage. A tattoo peeked out—a rose, probably red but appearing black in the bar's low light. She walked easily in her high heels, had the milky baby breasts that hormones grow. The drink she brought with her was blue and shimmery. Leave it to a girl like this to drink Blue Moons. She put it down right next to my martini.

"May I join you?" she said. Her smoky voice would, if heard over the phone, have given no clue as to her gender.

"Please," I replied, and scrambled to pull a chair from the next table over for her. She took a second to settle in. Close up I could see the brown roots showing in her cascade of honey-blond hair, could see her light lipstick carefully drawn on and the eyebrows plucked and shaped. Her skin was smoother than some of the others' and her hands were long. Her nails were clipped short—she was the only one I'd seen without long nails, I realized—but polished red. On her left hand she wore a ruby ring. There were two old gold wedding bands on her right.

"I've never seen you here before," she said. "At first I thought you might be here to watch one of your friends perform, but you don't seem to know anybody. Is this your first time?"

"My second," I said, and told her about Dave. She knew him, of course, and dropping his name had the same effect it had had with the doorman. It meant I was safe, in on the secret. Dave was one of the few guys a lot of the girls would date without exchanging money. I asked my new friend if she'd been out with him, mostly to make conversation. With a small smile, she shook her head.

"I don't date men," she said. "I work them."

That's how I met Ariel.

Before long I wondered if she was working me too. She was seductive, touching me while we talked, looking right into my eyes while I answered her questions. I had a hundred dollar bill in my pocket and I began to think about giving it to her. What fraction of the money she needed would one hundred dollars be? What would she want to do with me in return? I had some things I was trying to stop myself from thinking about the night I went to the Rose, and Ariel began to seem like a perfect way to forget them, better by far than ordering another martini or even sitting through the rest of the stage show.

"What are you thinking about, Miranda?"

"My intentions are becoming indecent. You're weaving quite a spell, Ariel."

"Oh, good." Ariel's hand, under the table, ranged up my thigh.

"The thing that has me confused is, are you working tonight? I mean, I know this is a working bar."

"I told you, I work men," said Ariel. She gestured around the bar, and indeed there were a lot of men there, all driven by their fascination with the queens. Some were dressed as workmen and some had on expensive suits; I remembered, as if I'd forgotten it, that I was the only one in the Rose who didn't have or had never had a cock. Once, I'd have thought of it as a place for closeted gay men. Now I knew it was more complicated than that. How I fit in as a genetic woman, though, wasn't at all clear to me.

But it was to Ariel. "I don't take money from women," she said. "I already made enough today. If you're feeling like a high-roller, you can buy me breakfast."

Ariel's apartment was close by, one of those beautiful old Tenderloin studios that you'd never expect to find in a rundown building on a mean street. The walk home with her screwed up all my butch-femme cues. Usually I'm femme-of-center, if not aspiring to diva-hood, myself. Tonight, I think out of my desire to melt into the woodwork at The Black Rose, I'd butched it up a little—jeans and a leather jacket, flat shoes. Ariel was much more femme than me, yet she took up so much space. She strode up Jones like it belonged to her, and I felt small by her side, like I needed her protection. She held the door for me, and then I held the elevator for her. This walk wasn't giving me any clues about who might do what to whom.

Inside she bolted the door, kicked off her heels, and pushed me up against the hallway wall. She kissed me hard while she pulled my jacket off, leaving it in a heap on the floor. Her long hands unbuckled my belt and tugged up my shirt, mouth never leaving mine, and I touched her through the slippery, glossy fabric of the clothes she wore. When I got to her breasts I felt the firm enclosure of a push-up bra trapping them into cleavage—she moaned when I found the clasp and freed them, rubbing away the marks of the underwires, raising her nipples up with strokes of my palms. And still we kissed.

Up 'til then it had been an experiment, but her kiss bought and sold me. I wondered how often she found women who wanted her, how long it had been since she'd brought someone home for play, not work, how many she had to convince and what she had to do to overcome the voices in their heads clamoring, "But she's not really a..."

That's not exactly what my inner voices had been clamoring. Like I said, I had some things I was looking to forget. But five minutes into what felt like the sweetest, hungriest kiss I'd ever been lost in, still leaning together against the inside of her apartment door, I'd forgotten everything except this tall, sexy tornado who was sweeping me away from everything, whose small new breasts just filled my hands, who had my nipples between her fingers, pulling, while she devoured my mouth and my cunt got wetter and wetter.

Her bed had red sheets. It glowed like a ruby in the pale room, and finally she led me there, pulled the rest of my clothes from me, and told me to put my hands over my head and hold onto the bars of the headboard. "I won't need to tie you," she purred, "if you're a good girl and stay right there." For an instant I wanted to disobey her—to feel her bind me, capture me, maybe get rough—but in the end I did what she said, wanting to please her, wanting to show her I was there, hot for her, there because I wanted to be.

Now I knew why Ariel groomed herself differently from the long-nailed queens at the Rose. She spread my legs wide, pulled on a latex glove, reached across me to the nightstand for lube, and then began working fingers into my ass. "Don't move your hands," she whispered, while hers invaded me, one long finger at a time, first working in and then starting to fuck—repeating again and again until she had three up my ass and I was as stretched out and full as I'd ever been. Her other hand, ruby ring glinting in the low light from a streetlamp, lay splayed across my belly, holding me down, thumb slowly working my clit, while she fucked my ass with the other. I held the bars but soon writhed crazily with the sensation, and as she fucked me more and more fiercely I raised my legs to her shoulders, spreading my ass as wide to her as I could, wanting to let her get at me as deeply as possible. When she felt my body tighten up in an imminent come, she stopped playing with my clit altogether, pulled my nipple hard, and I orgasmed from her pumping hand alone, coming until I was curled up practically sobbing—but still holding the bars.

"You're so good!" I gasped when she was finally done with me, and she gave me that small smile again and said, "What I like about assholes is, everybody has one."

I still didn't know if she had a cock. After she had my ass I lay panting and swimming in the afterglow of all the sensation, 'til finally I had recovered sufficiently to explore her. Her skin was soft, and she was an intriguing combination of curves and muscles, with a body that was not quite womanly.

I pulled her skirt off, ran my hands all over the firm swell of her ass, which she raised so I could get her panties off. Underneath I found still more fabric, a dense shiny lycra clinging tightly to the curve of her crotch. Rubbing my hand across it, like I would any pussy, Ariel writhed from the pleasure, then whispered, "Go ahead, take it off too."

The lycra peeled away and revealed it, still soft, the hair compressed around it from the tight gaffe she wore to hide its bulge. Was this the moment men paid her for, to see the unimaginable—a cock on a woman? Was she ashamed of it?

"Nice clit, girl," I breathed, petting it top to bottom so it stayed, for the moment, in its tucked and flattened position. "Big." Ariel's laugh didn't have any shame in it, and before long her big clit was in my mouth, getting only a little hard as I flicked my tongue across it. "Can you come this way?" I raised my head long enough to ask, and she nodded, gasped, "But I hardly ever ejaculate any more." I worked a couple of fingers up her ass while I worked her clit, and I knew when she came because her hips rose up off the bed and her hands clutched at the red sheets.

She came again, and so did I, over and over, when she rolled me onto the bottom and thrust against me like a classic tribade, her sex and mine rubbing ecstatically together. She got a little harder doing this, but not much, and it felt perfect, her ass in my hands, rocking and humping, while we kissed or sucked up red roses of blood nearly to the surface of each others' necks.

She brought me coffee in the morning. There she was in the light of day, makeup off, naked, still easily six feet tall, rangy and baby-titted like an adolescent. Gorgeous in a way I'd never seen anyone be gorgeous before. After only one night with her I was starting to see the world and its possibilities in a new way.

"Ariel," I began, "I've got a million questions to ask you..."

"Don't they all," she said, but she kissed me.

I started to ask them over breakfast.

goddess love

KATYA ANDREEVNA

"I don't really care what you think," Sheila said and stomped out the door of my apartment.

I got up from the couch to follow her, but stopped at the threshold. My nose was running and my eyelids throbbed. I held on to the doorknob and let the salt drip down my face. Our monthly fight was over. As usual, Sheila was off to seek solace in the arms of another woman.

I was left with the shards of the mug Sheila had thrown earlier and a pounding headache. I splashed my face with cold water and dug out the dustpan from the hall closet. It was only one in the afternoon and yet I was powerfully drawn to my bed. I could not let myself sleep.

"Yoga class," I thought and checked my wallet. Slumped in a chair, I counted out seven one-dollar bills. I was three dollars short. I sat staring. I couldn't stay in the house, not with the echoes of our fight bouncing around my head. I went to find my emergency money. This, I decided, qualified as an emergency. I opened the old candy tin with the Canadian Mounty on it, expecting to find the twenty I kept there. A few stray shirt buttons, some political campaign pins, no money.

"Damn, Sheila. She is probably treating some girl to drinks this very moment. Then late tonight or tomorrow she will come crawling back and expect me to nurse her 'bad stomach.' " She never used the word hangover. But then again, neither did I.

My nose started to drip again and my eyes clouded. I held the gold locket around my neck, trying to warm the cold metal. In my mind's eye, I saw them, standing at a bar, Sheila telling a charming story and she, the other woman, bending her head and laughing. Then they ordered fresh drinks.

I thought to call my friend Marcia, but I knew I couldn't. She wouldn't understand. She didn't know how much Sheila loved me.

"Did she hurt you?" she'd asked me the one time I had called her after one of our fights.

"Well, I'm upset," I had responded.

"I mean did she hit you? That's what I'm asking," Marcia had said.

I grabbed my coat and plunged out the door. The cool air soothed my burning cheeks. I cut through the icy park and kept going. The faster I walked, the faster I needed to walk or so it felt. As if I could out pace my thoughts, leave them behind me. The cool metal of the locket danced between my breasts. I made the mistake of turning up Second Avenue.

I hit the slow-moving pedestrian traffic of the street junk mall. This was where Sheila had bought me the locket. Well, not exactly. On the summer day I had spotted it, a shining heart, sandwiched between some old CDs and a useless electric coffee pot, I had asked her for it.

"What do you want a piece of junk like that for?" she had said and laughed. "We all know that emotions come from the brain, not the heart."

I went back, though, and bargained for it. Later that week, after I had cut Sheila's hair, I stashed one of her dark curls in the hollow of my new ornament.

The snowy sidewalk was littered with rows of crumpled shoes, wrinkled blouses, stained dresses. Passersby gawked at the shoddy merchandise as if they were viewing famed museum relics. I twisted past several groups of them only to be stopped by a mound of old electric gadgets. I hopped sideways to get around the bulky objects, but my foot caught and I fell, catching myself on my hands and skinning my palms.

"Oh, lady, let me help you, lady," the man who minded the pile of junk that had felled me crooned. He stood over me and made no move to assist me. I stayed where I was for a few seconds, face to the pavement, collecting myself, squeezing any sloppy tears back into their ducts.

I raised my head slowly. Where I expected to see a man in a hooded sweatshirt and dirty jeans, the Goddess Durga reared up before me. Panic spread through my chest. I crouched on the ground. Had I hit my head? I wondered and gingerly patted my scalp. I snuck another look up at her. Her lovely arms seemed to dance about her head—all five pairs of them. Her cool eyes glittered down at me. Her form was brilliantly carved in fluid lines. I looked around quickly to see if any of the shoppers had noticed my silly fright.

"You're even scared of a statue." In my head I heard Sheila's voice. *"So why would your fear of me mean anything?"*

I stood up slowly. The man still hovered near me. I couldn't take my eyes from the image of Durga. Finally, I croaked, "How much for the Goddess?"

"For you, lady, seven dollar. Only seven dollar."

I was convinced. Somehow he knew that seven dollars was the only money I had. Surely, then, this statue was to be mine. I handed him my wadded bills and lifted the Goddess from her seat of honor among the electronics.

Although she only stood two-feet high, she was heavy. Rushing home the way I had come, I worried that I would run into Sheila, that she would mock me for buying such a piece of trash.

"She'll be jealous," I thought. Notions like that made me worry that I was losing my mind.

I struggled up the stairs with my Durga. She seemed to grow heavier with each step. Oddly enough, her weight kept shifting. She didn't feel like an inanimate object. She felt more like a cat in a bag. A very heavy cat.

I fussed around the apartment, finding the right place for my new treasure. When she was finally settled against the east wall of my bedroom, I collapsed in a heap on the floor and looked at her. And then I started to cry. The Mack truck of my troubles, temporarily lost on the road, had found me, knocked me down, and now it waited, idling, wheels on my chest. My sobs forced words out of me, things I didn't know I knew, thoughts I didn't know I had.

She will kill me. Steals from me. Loves me. Wants me unhappy. Needs me. Have no friends. Won't let me talk. Suicide. Need to leave. Not safe. She has keys. She made me. I didn't want to. It hurt.

Hiccups racked through me, tearing at my lungs. As I held my cold, gold heart in my hands, I became aware of a rustling noise. My first instinct was to hide. "Sheila must be in the house," I thought.

A sinuous arm draped around my shoulders, another supported the small of my back. My breathing became more regular, as Durga pulled me to her. She smiled at me and I was not afraid despite the strangeness of this occurrence. I circled an arm around her waist. Animated, she was just slightly taller than me.

"You grew," I said and then felt like an idiot.

"I am always the right size for the task at hand," the Goddess responded. She cradled me in her arms, stroking my back. She rocked me as the last tears oozed down my cheeks. My tears spent, she massaged my neck and my feet at the same time. With each stroke of her many hands, I felt the fear and embarrassment that had gripped my body melting. And as they left, strength and determination took their place.

Gently the Goddess removed my clothes. She laid me down on the floor and caressed my naked torso. I was surprised by the warmth that began to spread from my loins into my belly.

"Should I be turned on by this?" I thought.

"Don't worry," the Goddess said. "Enjoy."

She lowered her body over mine, pressing her full breasts against my own. She pinned my arms down with one set of hands, stroked my flanks with another. She nuzzled my neck and, when she began to plant little kisses along my collar bone, I giggled. I couldn't remember feeling so relaxed with another person. I knew I would not have to defend myself against Durga. She would stop when I wanted to, if I wanted to.

Making love with Sheila I was always on guard against the moment her passion would turn to force. Vigilant against my own reactions least they provoke the porcupine of her anger and thus leave me full of quills.

Durga rolled off of me. She untied her feather-covered blouse. Her naked, round breasts left me breathless. I cupped one in both hands and brought my face to it worshipfully. She pulled on the chain of my locket with her teeth.

"What are you doing?" I asked.

"Warming your heart," she said. She sucked the locket into her mouth.

And I did feel warmer, but perhaps it was all the pairs of hands that teased my flesh. A pair of hands stroked my knees and inner thighs. While my buttocks were squeezed, fingers combed lovingly through my bush. My breasts sung under Durga's capable fingers. There was too much sensation for me to take it all in and yet my whole body cried out for more.

Durga smiled at me and began to part my slick labia. She tugged on my inner lips and slid a finger around the opening of my honeyed hole.

"Oh, yes, Goddess," I murmured. I shuddered with pleasure as her fingers reached inside me. She moved slowly at first, but then her speed and force increased. Eyes closed, I panted beneath her. With each stroke of her fingers, I felt myself grow. Her energy poured into me. Awash in pleasure, I couldn't tell where my body ended or began. I raised my head from the floor.

Durga rubbed my earlobes and temples with one pair of hands. Another set played a feather around the nipples of my quivering breasts. As I surveyed my body, I found that somehow I could see myself from all sides at once. I watched one of Durga's hands pumping into my open, wet pussy, while a pair of her palms worked the backs of my thighs, and another hand added fire at my swollen love button. My excitement mounted when I realized that yet another hand played at the opening of my anus.

I wanted more. As I shifted down, forcing her fingers deeper inside my cunt, I saw her tenth hand disappear between her own legs. I reached for that hand, drew the fingers away from her cunt, and sucked the juices from them slowly. The taste of her, salty and sweet, inflamed me further. I cupped her furry love mound with one hand, then dipped my fingers into the wet inside. Her clit throbbed under my fingers. She moaned softly and rocked her hips toward me all the while working my body into a frenzy with her hands. I could stand no more. I gasped for air. My whole being shook. A release that I never imagined possible washed over me. My body was both expanding and contracting at the same time.

Durga encircled me in her arms until my shaking subsided. I held one of her hands in both of mine. I took the fingers that had been inside me into my mouth and licked and sucked. She rubbed my bottom and continued to fuck my hungry mouth. She laid me down on my stomach. I opened to her and she slid inside my asshole. She wiggled her finger and set shocks of delight throughout my system. I raised my hips to meet her hand and bucked against her fingers.

"Gently," the Goddess said.

"More," I pleaded. I climbed to all fours and she leaned over me, her hot breasts resting on my back, her beautiful hand penetrating the dark of my shithole. I ground myself against her. All too soon I was panting, twitching, howling. My ears began to ring. My face and my whole body flushed. Convulsing, I collapsed to the floor, my pussy fluttering. Durga's hands patted my back. The exhaustion that I had expected to overtake me did not come. Despite, or perhaps because of the expenditure of energy, I was filled with strength.

I gazed up at my Goddess. She grinned when my hands glided

between her thighs. She knelt in front of me, knees wide and I buried my tongue in her tasty wetness. I lapped her juices, sucked her clit, and slid my tongue deep, where I felt her ripples of pleasure. She came in a gush. I drank her in, gulping and struggling to breath.

She lay down next to me, squeezed me tight. Her hands fixed my hair, traced the bones of my face, ran a feather along the outline of my lips.

"This will not happen again," she said and I detected a note of reluctance in her voice, "but know that I am with you always." She rose to her feet.

I struggled to sit up, to reach out, to call her name, but found I could not move. My eyelids dropped closed.

What seemed like moments later, I woke with a start. A two-foot Durga stood unmoving against the wall of my bedroom. Her eyes shown brightly. I followed her gaze to where the phone book lay on the floor. I turned to locksmiths, called, and arranged to have my locks changed that afternoon.

Stretching out on the floor to wait for the locksmith, my hand brushed something soft. I rolled over and found one of the Goddess's feathers. Opening my precious locket, I thought I felt a pulse in the warm metal. I removed the lock of Sheila's hair and slipped the yellow feather inside.

so generously
BETH BRANT

Even now, the texture of your voice over the phone covers me with memory of your silk-brown skin, your nipples brushing my own, your tongue marking trails on my neck, my mouth, my shoulders. Your breath in my ear—*"Te amo."* The sound of your voice this night has carried me to the place of writing.

I told you then I would write poems to you.
Years later, I am writing this one.

Something I could give you—years after our heated, rushed love, spanning only thirty days—the residue of those nights and days remains inside me like the scent from the passion-soaked sheets lingered in your room.

I spread my legs and my body to you. I spread my self to you, opening and opening to every touch and word you caressed on me.

"Te amo," you whispered. *"Mi corazón,"* you sang.

Your fingers on my back as we danced, the brush of your hand on my arm as we rode the subway, the way you held a book, the way you moved, the way you talked, the color of your eyes—like black stones found in the sea; wet, beautiful, full of story. All these made heat rise in me.

Hot for you, wet for you.

My wetness; flowing, waiting to coat your fingers and hands, your lips and tongue.

Hot for you. Wet for you.

Kissing me as you rose from my open thighs, I would taste the liquid of myself on your tongue.

You made tapes of Willie Colon, Luciecita, Armando Reyes—knowing I would never listen to this music again without remembering the humidity of your room—candles lit, flowers placed in front of the image of *La Virgen*, bowls of water and salt flanking her picture. The dish of sand from your beloved Puerto Rico, the rosary of your mother laid across the white cloth. Each day you placed bread upon this altar.

I watched your hands perform this act of love, then turned to receive your body in another act of love.

You asked me to run away with you to your island. I imagined your land as you wove the descriptions to me. I could smell the water surrounding your land as I touched your breasts. I could taste the fruits of your land as I put my fingers inside you, then licked the cream that poured from you.

I knew I would not run with you, but I imagined your island.

And told you I would write poems to you.

Poems that would detail our meeting:

"I only fall for women who have Scorpio rising," you joked.

"I have Scorpio rising," I said.

Your confident, loud laughter as you took my hand and kissed my life-line.

"Somehow, I knew that," and your lips burned the lines that mapped across my palm.

Poems that would describe the Staten Island ferry, the restaurants we ate in, the New York stories, your neighborhood of pimps and junkies tangled with new Yuppies who came to exorcise the streets.

Poems about the presents you gave me—the topaz earrings, the flowers, the ring from Guatemala, the Tarot cards, the silk blouse you bought because it was the color of my eyes.

"A blue-eyed Indian," you sighed as you kissed my eyelids.

"Tell me about this blue-eyed Indian." And I told you secrets about myself.

Secrets I knew would be guarded by you.

Poems about the food you cooked for me. The sauce of garlic and oil that coated the *plátanos, yami,* and *chocho* with an opaque sheen. The *carne* stews, the rice, the thick, black coffee you boiled on the stove, adding sugar and milk until it became a confection.

Poems about your political activism for Puerto Rican independence, your Marxist-feminist analysis of everything, the gentleness towards your sisters who were locked in prison and whom you visited as often as possible; carrying sweets and flowers that were inevitably confiscated, but you persevered and fought for the right of beauty in that ugly world.

Poems that were scented with the sweat underneath your large breasts, the liquid between your legs, the black curling hair of your cunt, the dark mauve of your clitoris before you came, the salty-sweetness of your back.

Poems about your tenderness and roughness, the glorious reveling in our sex, the love words, the sex words whispered between us— Spanish and English mingling like our smells—lush vapor, close in your magic room.
"Say it, say it," you whispered between my legs.
And I would speak with waves upon waves of orgasm, my body shaking and soaring into a land of tropical heat and dust-covered roads, canopies of trees, sounds of ocean lapping against sand.

I was going to write poems to you.
Years later there is this.

Each day was going to be my last with you.
Your voice, heavy with sex, *"Te amo,"* and I would postpone the journey home.
I had come here when the air was still cold, snow falling outside Gloria's apartment, and too soon the trees in Central Park began leafing new green, the whores on Alphabet Street were shedding coats to better display their skinny bodies to customers, the junkies were nodding off in the sun.

It was not my intention to give anything up, especially myself.
Nor did I.

I had no intentions, no plans, no wishes.

Your call was fierce, sweet, and my answer mirrored your fierceness, matched your sweetness.

Our last night, the candles burning a hot, steady flame, you again touched every part of me that could bring pleasure. You held my face in your hands and licked the tears—a mixture of yours and mine.

"Women leave me. Why?"

Now, as we talk on the phone from time to time, your voice raised in outrage at the latest political atrocity, the latest homophobic attack, you recite the latest failed relationship—married women, straight women, unfaithful women.

Exasperated, I say that you only find what you are looking for, women who will always leave you.

"You don't want a solid relationship," I say, "only ones that will prove your ability to make a conquest."

"*Sí, querida,*" you say. "So, when are you coming to New York again?"

You laugh, and in my mind's eye, I see your full, dark lips drawn across your white even teeth, and I want to feel those lips on mine and on my body, sucking my breasts, sucking out the honeyed liquid that flows so readily at the sound of your voice.

I laugh with you.

"I have never made love with a grandmother," you say teasingly.

"You must be losing your touch."

"I haven't lost my touch, *mi corazón.* Perhaps you have just forgotten it."

I have not forgotten your touch. It comes to me at times I least expect—a gift from the conscious past—wrapped in brown silk and carrying the smell of botanicas where we purchased candles and magic herbs. I have not forgotten your touch.

We have seen each other through the years—at conferences, at seminars. I am always careful to not be alone with you, except in the safe places of cafés. You send me birthday cards and presents each May. We talk on the phone, your calls taking place during the day when you know I will be alone.

I keep your letters and cards in a special place, alongside the topaz earrings, the take-out menu from Ming Gardens, the dried roses from the bouquet you gave me at the airport on our last day in New York.

But even in the safety of cafés, your gestures and voice bring back memory of wet nights, wet bodies, wet places of love. The smell of you as you labored to bring forth every sensation from my being.

Reaching into my body for response, your hands entering all parts of me and your whispers of *"Te amo, te amo.* Speak to me, *querida.* Say it, say it."

I spoke in the language of my body.
The speech of my willing skin.
The dialect of my swollen nipples.
The accent of breath upon soft thighs.
The phrases of shouts and sighs of joy and release.

Years later, I give this poem to you.
It is small next to your abundance of spirit.
So generously you loved me.

I give this to you.
And you will know, *querida,* this is yet another way to say *"Te amo."*

collision course: an excerpt

María Helena Dolan

By the time Gloria arrives at the party, Octavia has already been hard at work for an hour or so, legs spread slightly apart, one hand anchored on her thrust-out hip, the other clutching a drink, her open mouth, even the inclination of her head, all saying "Take me. Fuck me. Use me. *Make* me come. Now."

Gloria is as dark as Octavia is light. Her well-oiled, cafe-au-lait-colored skin glistens across defined muscles, hard-won from years of carpentry and sweat in the gym. Her dark eyes stare piercingly, a perfected look that has been known to turn women into pliant puddles while they clutch at their pissed-off dates.

Gloria's height commands attention, as does her ass. It's covered in fine black silk, daring a hand to run across fabled contours. This ass is an engineering marvel, high and firm and succulent. She often quips that, if she were a white girl, she wouldn't be able to sit, 'cuz white girls just don't have the right kind of support.

This white girl bears a respectable ass though, Gloria thinks. They surreptitiously eye each other for long, considered moments. For her part, Octavia thinks that she'd like to press that high, fine ass hard with her hands as the butch grinds against her. Yes.

While it's true that this bitch has that stringy-ass white-girl thin blond hair, it isn't her hair that interests Gloria.

Having been "in the game" for most of three decades now, Gloria is a good judge of woman flesh. In one slow, sweeping glance, Gloria takes it all in. She can tell: 1) the bitch is definitely hot to trot, 2) she'll do anything I tell her to, 3) she's trouble, big time. She never has done right, she never will do right, and you're crazy if you want more than one night with her.

But Gloria would climb imposing mountains, swim endless oceans, hurdle all barriers, kill if she must, to have that one night, here and now.

Octavia radars in on the handsome black butch in soft black silk looking her over as if she's already made the down payment, and the installment's come due. She can virtually feel those strong hands running over her flesh, and then entering her body with incredible ferocity.

Oh, she longs to be fucked by someone who knows just how to do it; and this one clearly does. It's self-evident from the way the woman holds herself, barely containing the roiling passions coursing through her blood. It's self-evident from her very stance; her legs apart, balanced on the pads of her feet, ready to spring, her arms crossed to keep from reaching under and up. It's self-evident from the look in her eyes, which tells smoldering stories about an everlasting hunger, a never-ending search for fulfillment, a continual take-no-prisoners sweeping action.

And that mouth. Octavia could almost taste the kisses, the full lips crushing her own, that long, pink tongue—currently flicking teasingly out of the corner of that to-die-for mouth—reaching down deep into her throat.

And then working across her pulsing clit. She wants that dark head between her legs. She wants to feel every bit of it. All of it. She wants to soak that handsome face with her juices.

But most of all, Octavia wants to perform. She wants to perform so desperately, so achingly. She wants to scream and scream, to spur that butch on. She wants to cry and moan, to spur the butch on. She wants to get so wet that the sheets need wringing, to spur the bitch on. She wants to shudder and shake and convulse, to spur the bitch on. She wants to come and come, to ensnare the bitch.

* * *

Octavia grew up poor and propertyless, with a different name, in a tiny town in southern Louisiana. This meant that, yeah, you didn't have shit, but at least you were white. And black had better not look at you. And you didn't need to look at them, either.

But moving to Nawlins brought considerable changes. Someone named Florence Mae left the daily petty assaults that come with having nothing; left the horror of years of older brother and uncle incest; left the hopelessness and complete lack of a future; and constructed an entirely new self.

She was smart, and a quick study. She worked hard, and learned. She saw how white girls with real class walked, talked, dressed. She studiously copied them. She took a new name with a historic cachet, and invented a new past with just a few "colorful" echoes of what she'd left behind.

Florence-Mae-now-Octavia hung out in the Vieux Carre, and befriended the transvestite hookers. Newly constructed themselves, they embraced her as a sister. They taught her about high femme and happily instructed about the effects of the tiniest nuances with great flourish and care.

So she combined what she'd learned about high class and high femme, and the effect proved devastating on butches all across the South. Not Yankees of course. No, that's a whore of a different color.... And color changes in Nawlins. Black and white mix there. Not all the time, not always positively. But it was clearly uncool in this adopted milieu to retain those metal-roof ideas.

Atlanta beckoned. Lots of jobs, lots of women, lots of opportunities to remake herself again and again. She'd honed her skills, until she could wield them like a razor. And so she settled for the paradox that has no resolution; let them all touch you, while none ever really touches you.

Let yourself be fucked senseless and appear open; but it's the openness of the Venus Flytrap. Once the fly, attracted by the scent of sweet decay, lands on the rim, she tumbles in and is digested.

* * *

Gloria's entire life has also led her to this very moment. She had invented herself, too. Her people had been in Atlanta since slave time. They had bought their freedom, they had "done well," they had been pillars of the community for generations, they were the embodiment of the Talented Tenth.

But Gloria was a change child. She was raised with every advantage and every demand known to her community in segregated life. Daddy had a slew of businesses, Mama graduated from Spelman, and they both sat on more boards than a lumber mill could saw.

Mama and Daddy had Big Plans for their oldest and only daughter. But events caught up with them. Gloria was one of the first to attend integrated schools. She went from not being able to try on dresses at Rich's to having a personal shopper from Rich's submit clothes for her approval in Gloria's office.

She went to Smith instead of Spelman. She received offers from all sorts of corporations, settling on Coca Cola for the home-town appeal, even though "Cocola" sent her to oversee operations in Europe.

Inevitably, Gloria discovered the downsides of tokenism. She'd always had a sense of self, a sense of place before. Now, she was in a white world, and it was pretty openly hostile—or worse yet—subtly so. She tired of always looking for the hidden messages, the real stories, the true meanings in things white folk said or did. She learned to curry acceptance, but she made sure the dealin' didn't touch her.

She also learned the upside of tokenism. She could make the bitches want her, want her so badly that they begged for it, want her so badly that they lost all sense, want her so badly that they would give her anything: hearts, money, souls, gifts, even jobs.

Finally, she decided she would just try to please herself from here on out. If she pleased a few femmes along the way, so much the better.

* * *

Tonight, Gloria feels it in her face, her hands, her breasts, her belly, her cunt, her legs. She aches to roll over and over a woman's body, to give and receive pleasure, to wrap some bitch's legs around her head and make that cunt give it up.

Oh yeah, she wants to eat pussy so bad she can hardly stay inside her own skin. She wants to put her hand inside the bitch and pump away until she begs for mercy, and keep pumping until she begs for more. She wants to make the bitch scream her name over and over, crying and praying and sobbing. She wants to squeeze her flesh so tightly that the bitch comes away with bruises. She wants the bitch to take her fist, and her dick, and love it. And she wants this bitch, standing here so self-possessed, so waving-it-in-her-fucking-face.

As if no one else is in the room, Gloria glides over, and stands close enough to Octavia that their quickening breaths meet in the air, and draw into each other's lungs. "Great stockings," she purrs, ebony eyes never leaving blue ones. Octavia smiles.

"Great legs, too," Gloria continues, eyes still locked, unblinking, penetrating. Color rises a bit in Octavia. "Thanks—I grew them myself," she manages to tease out, with a devastating, practiced flip of her hair.

Gloria reaches down, touches the hem of the miniskirt, and lifts it an inch or so, eyes still locked. "Does that pattern continue all the way up?" she inquires nonchalantly. "I guess you'll have to see for yourself," Octavia replies huskily. "I intend to. Why don't you show it to me now?" she almost commands, lifting the hem another inch or so, still staring into pools of sky.

"Here?" Octavia almost squeaks. "No," Gloria calmly reassures. "My place. It isn't far, and I guarantee you'll find it more entertaining than anything else here tonight."

Intrigued, but not wanting to appear to give it up too readily, Octavia answers, "How can you be so sure? I was planning on doing some dancing..."

"I've got quite a collection of tapes. And you can dance anywhere you like: the living room, the dining room, the bedroom, or my face."

"Aren't you forward."

"No, actually I'm Gloria, and I'm also just clear about what I want."

"And what might that be?" Octavia teased in high-femme formation, head flung back, breasts thrust forward, hips a little restrained by the hand still holding her skirt. "You," Gloria immediately replied. "I want you. Now. All night long. I want you in my arms. I want you with your legs spread around me. I want to make love to you. I want to lick your pussy. I want you."

Octavia could barely suppress a groan, imagining how all that would feel. "You don't waste any time," she admonished. "Haven't we wasted enough already?" Gloria asked, an arching eyebrow following the rise in her voice.

Octavia smiles, and says, "You don't even know my name."

"I know who you are, Octavia. And I know what you are."

Surprised, Octavia wonders, "What do you mean..."

Gloria interrupts, "You're looking for me tonight. That's enough. Now I'm going to turn your skirt loose, and you're going to pick up your jacket, and come with me."

* * *

In what seem like only moments, they arrive at a huge old house on the edge of the park. This Victorian is impressive in her restored grandeur, a true Empress Dowager who retains her looks while acquiring a century of massive grace.

The already lit vista is amazing. Woodwork gleams everywhere, from floor to ceiling and back around again. And this is just the entryway. Perfunctorily, but with some pride, Gloria describes a few of the most spectacular appointments.

Sincerely impressed with the place, Octavia asks, "And you did all this yourself?"

Gloria shrugs, and replies, "Mostly." She drops her voice an octave, and continues, "I'm very good with my hands."

"We'll see about that," Octavia sniffs, holding her arms out slightly so Gloria will help her off with her jacket.

"How about some music then? Marvin Gaye okay?"

"Yes, I love him, those cool high falsettos, and all that growly feeling in his voice that he puts out so smoothly."

Good thrust, Gloria thinks, nodding. Time to parry. She puts on the custom tape, and advances on Octavia.

Gloria extends her arms forward in a commanding but inviting gesture, and Octavia comes to her with compliant eagerness. They wrap arms around each other, and their mouths find each other.

This kiss, so slow and wide and easy and wet, becomes a shock, a five-alarm fire, the Big Quake an entire coast has been waiting for. Surprised at how good it is, Gloria finds an obscure part of her brain shouting, "Everything will burn!!" Octavia's hips begin to roll with the intensity of the heat. She can't help it, or even exercise a conscious act of will to make them stop.

They somehow find their way to the couch, touching, stroking, exploring, kissing kissing kissing. Enflamed, Gloria's hand drags up that trembling thigh, trailing the flame to its place of origin. Then it finds that astonishingly soft pussy hair, and Gloria wants to cry, it feels so good. Octavia gasps as fingers dance on the very edges of her hair.

Unable to restrain themselves any longer, Gloria's fingers touch the base of the hairs, and the place they spring from, the creviced lips extending down in a smooth curve.

Gloria's forefinger finds the tip of Octavia's clit. Octavia gasps and pushes against that knowing finger, which now teases across her stiffening flesh.

Her finger is soon joined by the thumb, and they begin to tease and squeeze. Octavia feels her eyes roll back in her head with this sensation. Gloria unlocks her other hand from behind Octavia.

Freed to do its own bidding, this hand seeks the softness of Octavia's breast. First, the camisole strap is peeled away. Then, the push-up bra is pulled down, so the small mounds can ride out in the open. The hand covers a tit, exploring the miracle of woman flesh. Already, the nipple is hard.

The hand cups, kneads, strokes, then fingers press the nipple and roll it. Octavia twitches, her hips a seething mass, her tit on fire.

Somehow, Gloria unlocks her mouth from Octavia's, and it flies to that breast. Her lips and tongue kiss and rub while her fingers continue to squeeze.

Suddenly, Gloria sits up, removing her mouth and hands. Octavia is shocked. "Get on the floor," she tells Octavia. "Face the couch, on your knees," Octavia slides off the couch, skirt revealing more than concealing, breasts thrust out. She kneels.

Gloria kneels behind Octavia, mouth working that neck, hands working both breasts.

When one hand reaches under her skirt and begins stroking her clit, Octavia cries out. She feels Gloria pressed against her back, feels those hands on her, feels those teeth on her neck, and wants more. She leans forward against the couch, ass in the air, swaying with the movement of her shifting hips. She feels her own wetness and pounding need.

Just entering this woman's body sends a shock through Gloria. As she feels the pleasure and the need and hears the shrieks and commands, Gloria can't believe how good this is, and she can think of nothing beyond giving this woman whatever she wants. She keeps on, in and out, in and out, furiously delivering each stroke as if life itself depended upon it, knowing nothing else but this.

With one hand wailing away inside her, and the other squeezing her now enormous clit, and that mouth biting down her bare shoulders and back and that body pressing against her, Octavia lets loose her orgasm with a screaming roar. Her entire body strains as she comes in a frenzy; she only stays at all upright because her hands clutch the couch.

* * *

Suddenly, she's aware of a presence, and looks up to see Gloria, handing her a glass, swathed in the most amazing powder-blue silk Chinese robe ever seen, emblazoned with two mirror-image black dragons devouring white-hot suns. Octavia is struck by the woman's taste and beauty. "Drink," she is told.

After a few sips, Gloria indicates she should put that glass down, and Octavia does. Gloria slowly opens the robe, the top first, and Octavia sees two wonderful, full mounds, the dusky midnight of the nipples contrasting with the dark brown of the breasts. There's a tattoo between the breasts, which she can't make out clearly from her angle.

Awe-inspiring muscle definitions begin just below the tits and make curved, even furrows across her terrain, until they reach the swell above her triangular patch, and that...that black strap-on, which looks more like a weapon than a toy!

"Get on your knees, and show me you know what to do with this. Make it wet so I can stick it inside you." Octavia freezes for an instant. Then she gets on her knees and crawls over to Gloria's legs. She kisses the thighs, rubbing her cheek against the chiseled hardness, easing a hand up the back to that marvelous ass.

Pulling on Octavia's hair and thus forcing her head back, Gloria just says, "Eat it," and Octavia takes it in her hands, and opens her mouth to the shaft. Back and forth she moves it into her mouth, eyes closed.

Gloria pushes on Octavia's head a little, and hisses, "You've done this before." Octavia looks up with those innocent baby blues, and keeps eating. Finally, Gloria pulls away, and plants her ass on the edge of the couch. "Sit on it, bitch. I want you to work for it."

Smiling, Octavia straddles the butch, first putting her cunt practically in Gloria's face, then rubbing her tits there. Finally, she takes the thing into her hand, and eases it into her pussy, crying out when it reaches deep. Gloria begins pumping her hips up and down, forcing the thing in and out. Octavia moans with each thrust, hands gripping Gloria's wrists, swaying atop those muscled thighs.

After a short while though, it becomes clear that Octavia just wants to lie there and be fucked, so Gloria grabs hold of the woman's hips, and lowers her to the floor. Gloria begins to fuck in earnest, and Octavia raises her knees to drive the dick deeper into her.

Gloria holds onto the woman by the shoulder blades, humping away like buildings on fire and raging out of control, like uncontrollable and uncontainable catalytic reactions, like dogs gone mad. Octavia responds in kind, sounding like a torture victim begging for release. Eventually, she gives it up and starts to come, feeling as though she is being split apart, with the crack starting in her cunt and widening as it travels up her body. But Gloria can't stop, she drives and drives through this extraordinary tunnel, knowing only that she must keep going.

Finally, Octavia screams, "Stop, stop! I can't stand any more." So Gloria stops, easing the thing out, panting and sweating, collapsing against the woman's body. They just lie together for a long time, holding on to one another, barely breathing.

Octavia whispers, "I want to taste you," and slides out from under Gloria.

"Let me take this thing off," Gloria says, and they both giggle. "Smells like you," Gloria teases as she tosses it aside.

"I'm not surprised," Octavia responds.

First, they kiss. Then Octavia heads south, with her cunt traveling up north and wriggling, beckoning, enticing. She plants herself on top of Gloria, presenting her cunt with a flourish.

Greedily, Gloria begins to lick, and Octavia presses her face down into the rough black curls. She pulls the lips apart, revealing purplish pink vistas. When she lifts the dark hood back, she's rewarded with the stunning pink beneath, and smiles.

Skillfully, steadily, she begins to move her tongue up and down, feeling the swelling and smelling the excitement. Continuing on, she barely feels the tongue working her, so intent is she upon this cunt. Harder now she presses, faster now she licks this landscape. The stiffening of Gloria's thighs and the moans echoing into her own pussy spur Octavia on.

Come on bitch, she thinks. *Come on and come all over me. Come on and show yourself. Come on and give it to me. Come on and come.*

Holding off as long as she can, Gloria finally surrenders to the sensation. Shouting incomprehensibly into Octavia's pussy, Gloria's body arches like a backflip diver as she still holds onto Octavia's legs, pushing her own cunt into Octavia's face.

Gloria trembles all over, convulses, tightens her muscles even more, flips Octavia completely over and onto her back, then presses hard against the woman's face as she continues to come with cataclysmic force, again and again.

Octavia smiles into Gloria's cunt, satisfied that this night has triumphantly brought her exactly what she wants.

candy calls star to her

CHERYL CLARKE

'Black gal!
Black gal!
Where you gone?
Git back here.
(I don't wanna face the dawn alone.)'

'Star. Star. Star.
Whatever you want.
Take my money,
my jewels, my furs.
Take it all
Just stay with me
this one night.
That ole yella witch got me scared
I always sees my funeral in her eyes.'

Star's resentment melted
and Candy showed her gold.

'Take that dress off.
fore you come in this bed.
No sense to get it wrinkled.
Cost too much money.'

Star bristled under the order.
And under Star's emerald stare

Candy lost her bald belligerence
again
and lay back,
her head against her purple pillow.
She let her breath out soft
watching Star unbutton the dress
against her own black nakedness.

'Gal, you gon ruin yo clothes
with sweat don't you wear nothing
under em.'

'I don't sweat.'

declared Star, climbing into Candy's bed
looking square at her.
They lay together silent—
Star staring through the ceiling
to the moon,
Candy staring at Star.

'Come on, Star. Take me
in your arms.
I ain't so tough
I can lay here and
not be touched.'

Star felt a gladness shake her
to her belly and rolled toward
Candy.
Star took her in her long arms,
heard Candy's breath of desire,
saw it part her buxom lips,
the glint of gold between them.
Star, having never kissed no one
but Mama, had no choice but to press
her longing lips against Candy's.
Her tongue found Candy's.
Candy helped Star's hand find
her pot of gold and her finger

imitated the motion of her tongue.
Candy reassured her.

    'That's right, baby.'

Baby, thought Star, *now I likes the way
that sound.*
Star rubbed, pressed, and squeezed.
Candy was an overripe peach.

    'Been so long since I had a woman
    in my bed, baby.'

Candy held Star hard against her
at the waist
and their bodies moved fast against
one another's.

Star heard Candy's heart beat like
Bussy's drum.
Then her legs jerked,
her back rose from the mattress.
Star felt fear, the same fear
she felt when she saw a cow give birth.
Candy screamed,

    'Glory!'

And Mourning Star Blue, no longer afraid,
burst into laughter for the first time
since she sang in the fields.

Candy said:

    'Go on, Star, laugh loud as you wanna.
    I'm gonna make you do it again.
    Then I'm gonna git you on the floor,
    baby. Better be ready for me.
    I'll hear yo secret high note tonight
    or you won't never sing it.'

Star repeated the lesson
then rolled off the edge of the bed
while Candy gasped.
Only the soles of her feet
and shoulders touching the floor,
Star's thighs flexed and made a
startling *V*.
Candy came to her,
slid on top,
her thigh planted between
Star's *V*.

> 'Wait, baby, hold on.
> Not yet. Let me show you.
> And then you can do it to me
> next.'

Star exhaled in short spurts
to the tickly darts of pain
in her groin.
Candy slid further down and placed
her mouth against the low part of the *V*,
her tongue broad-stroking Star
like she was a canvas.

> 'Wait, baby, wait.
> One more thing.'

Candy's thumb inside her,
Star understood her rhythm.
Hard and gentle.
In. Out.

> 'Baby, not yet. Turn over.'

Star was puzzled but obedient.
Candy parted her own wet pussy and
pressed it against Star's tight buttocks,
and rode her.
She wound her hand around and under

Star's vibrating groin
and found her spot again.
Star was very wet now.

> 'Okay, baby, I wanna hear
> that high note,
> now!'

And Star saw the saints,
heard the angels,
and took her place among them.
She knew she was dying
and heaven was the only place
she could go.
The note shattered every glass
in Candy's railcar.

> 'Jesus,'

whispered Star.

> 'Candy, baby.
> Jesus don't have nothing
> to do with this here,"

said Candy.
And then bit her hard in the ass.

> 'Yes, baby.
> No cross, no crown.'

Star whirled around
rubbing her butt
and pushed Candy back
on the floor
under her and dove for her stuff
face first.
For an hour Candy let Star lick,
suck, and chew.
And as Candy drew in her breath

and made ready for her glory shout,
Star pushed away from the table.
Candy jerked up in protest, gold gleaming.
Star laughed.

    'Yeah, Mama,
    no cross, no crown.'

D & D

KITTY TSUI

Dear Daddy and Doña:

One of my fantasies is being fucked by two tops. Are the both of you up for it? Another fantasy is being tied to a tree and getting flogged.

Love, boy nigel.

Dear boy nigel:

Let's get a little more specific, shall we? Daddy loves little boy's asses, while Doña loves their big cunts. Do you like dildos or fingers or fists? Doña also loves to chew on nipples and shoulders. And we're both oh so fond of canes and fire. How do you like it? One or the other orifice, both at once, or one and then the other? How do you like it? Leaning up against a tree, or on your hands and knees, spread and dripping? Or on your back, with four strong women holding you down? Tell us more....

D & D.

Dear Daddy and Doña:

Thank you for your letter which I read with great glee. This boy will try to answer your questions. I love dildos, fingers, and fists though I'm afraid of both canes and fire. Everything else that you suggested sounds wonderful too. My fantasy involves being fucked in front by Doña and from behind by Daddy. I will write more later. I am not feeling very well today but I wanted to get back to you right away. My chiropractor said that my soul is emerging and that causes nausea.

Love, boy nigel.

boy nigel:

Sorry that you are feeling nauseous, but it seems a good thing for your soul to emerge from the shell of pain you seem to have been inhabiting. As for your fantasy, let us be more direct: Daddy and Doña want *details*. To put it another way: you get what you ask for. Or to use a cliché: The squeaky wheel gets the oil. };>

Waiting, D & D.

P.S. And speaking of fear. Fear is a good thing. Fear can be very, hmmmmm, fun. The physical sensations that signal fear are very similar (and often the same) to those that signal sexual arousal. Mixing the two so that they become inseparable and/or using one to increase the other is one of the things D & D *really* like to do.

Dear Daddy and Doña:

Sorry I haven't replied sooner but now that I've put it out there to the Universe, I'm...well, I'm frightened. But, Sir and Madame, this boy has been well-trained so here goes:

I would like to be collared and tied to a tree. A tree with the *roughest* bark, please. I would like to be flogged on my back. Please, Sir and Madame, as hard as you can give it to me. Doña, I have small nipples and big shoulders. I would be honored if you would like to chew on them. Later I would like to have my briefs cut off me. I know you're both fond of canes and I will try to endure as you indulge yourselves on my ass and thighs. Excuse me, Sir and Madame, but I don't know how you are planning on playing with fire. Suffice to say that this boy will trust himself to the flames in your able hands. I will have my boy, matt, and he will take care of me and clean me up for your further pleasure. I would like Doña to fuck me in my cunt and Daddy to fuck me in my ass. *Please, Sir*, please be gentle at first as this boy has had neither a cock nor even a finger up his ass for the last three years. After you have both used me for your pleasure, I will have my boy clean me up. Then I will kiss your boots in gratitude. If you wish me to perform any other duty, I would be most glad to do so to the best of my ability. In closing, Sir and Madame, please know that if boy matt is needed for anything, he is also at your service.

I remain, faithfully, boy nigel.

Good boy!

We know that it is often hard to ask for what you want and you are to be commended on working through your fear and putting it out there.

D & D

P.S. Hullo, boy nigel, Daddy here. Of course I will be tender with your sweet ass. I shall have to give you extra attention. Three years without is much too long. Following are some instructions. For your future reference, when Daddy gives directions, he gives them only once, so listen:

Buy a small butt plug. If you can find one that's black or red, that's best. Black is the first choice, red follows, and then anything other than that "flesh" color. Of course if that's all you can find....

Second. Get a hair cut. Make sure that your clothes are pressed and your boots spit-shined. *Always* be perfectly presentable.

Third. Spend every moment on the drive up in anticipation.

Dear Randy and Amber:

Hey, listen you guys, I just got your last e-mail about final festival preparations and I'm *freaking* big time. Then I went and reread boy nigel's e-mail to you (yeah, the one that starts with being collared and tied to a tree) and now I'm really freaking. Did I say that? Did I actually write that and send it out on-line? What am I, nuts?! =:{ I gotta be. First of all, I've never *never* worn a collar. I'm petrified of canes. I mean, they fucking *hurt*. And to top it off, I'm afraid of fire. And to top that, to ask Daddy to ream my butt, I must be mad. Daddy has a big cock. Daddy has a huge cock and I was *not* joking when I said I haven't had anything up my ass for three years. Okay, I gotta rethink this. And the more I think about it, the more I think I *am* nuts and I better just call it off. Hey, I'm not afraid of losing face. I'd rather lose face than lose my hide. You got that right. Never mind negotiation, let's just forget it. Really, you guys, let's forget I mentioned anything okay? I must have been out of my mind. I must have been on an endorphin high. Okay, so now that I'm sane, just forget it.

Signed, Kate.

P.S. I'm serious, okay.

P.P.S. Dead serious.

Dear boy nigel:

Quit your ranting and raving and sit down. *Now.* Place your feet flat on the floor and put your hands in your lap. Close your eyes. Breathe in and out slowly. Breathe deep into your chest. As you exhale, let it out with a sound. Count your breaths. Do not think. When you arrive at the count of one hundred, get up and lay out your clothes and boots. Keep breathing. Dress yourself carefully. Go stand in front of the mirror. See yourself through Daddy and Doña's eyes. Trust us. Know that we will take good care of our boy. Put yourself into our hands.

Open yourself to adventure. The Universe awaits.

We will see you in the Twilight Zone at Michigan.

Come prepared.

Come dressed.

Come.

after the Bath

JENIFER LEVIN

With her dress—tight fit and dark leather straps—and heels high enough for drama but not too high to dance on, she looked nice standing on the sidelines in shadows and moving bodies, her mostly finished drink, wine I guess, held perfectly between fingers. We caught eyes and nodded.

"You don't dance, do you?" She got a cigarette and looked for matches, but I plucked some out of my own pocket sooner. Years ago some woman had stumbled up in a bar somewhere, eyelids heavy with booze, and asked for a light. Oh, I said, I don't smoke. She laughed. But honey, she replied, someone like you should always carry matches.

It had been sweet of her, really, to say that.

I'd carried them ever since, in various parts of the world. Hopefully.

Now, I lit one. Cassie touched my hand to steady it.

"Thanks."

I wanted to ask how she knew that—that I didn't dance. We recognized each other only vaguely, through parties, large dinners, friends of friends. The match did its job and I tossed it, then she was talking.

"Dell says some French girl broke your heart."

I didn't respond.

She shrugged. The dark smoke-filled place was kind to her. There were blurred old acne scars on each cheek. They must be deep because she'd used a lot of makeup. Even so she was pretty, nice lips, bright eyes. The lashes fluttered, sparking mischief.

"What's the story with Dell?"

"She thinks you're cute."

"Yucch! Damn me with faint whatchamacallit, why don't you? Anyway, she's got someone—right? Right. Of course."

"Would you like to dance?"

She thought about it. Then said yes, yes actually, that would be very nice. So we did. Two minutes into music you could bounce around to old sixties' style, manic, not touching, things segued into something slow. That's when fear stabbed and I got even clumsier. But she was smooth, Cassie was, and managed somehow to balance quietly without even the appearance of precariousness, patient, seeming to enjoy herself while I fought hesitation, adjusted my stance and all, and finally pressured the small of her back to lead. It was nice, a long, long song. After some of it I realized she'd laid her head against my shoulder. Her hands had found their way under the flaps of jacket, pressed lightly on silk shirt and ribcage. And underneath things, I was sweating.

"What do butches want?"

"Is that what I am?"

She pulled her head back a moment, eyes rolled mockingly. "Oh God, honey, come on." But she laughed.

"Well, what do you think?"

"I don't know—I'm curious. I mean, I like to watch you, all of you, everywhere, even when you're just standing still. I'd like to see what's going on in your head—I know it's different from what's going on in mine."

"Oh," I told her, "don't be so sure." Well, but then again, maybe.

What do we want? I thought.

You.

But said nothing.

Just before the song ended I caressed that part of her right on top of the place where buttocks meet thighs, very lightly, barely touching at all, and could tell that she felt it. We stood around talking then. I bought her more wine, lit more of her cigarettes.

Dell came by, looking irritated in new silks and leather and linen, and a pair of fur shoes colored black and white. She said hi to Cassie, pulled me aside. "Can you lend me twenty? I met someone, I want to buy her a drink. I think she might go to bed with me tonight."

"Congratulations."

"This place is really getting on my nerves. Maybe I ought to leave. Maybe I ought to take a Xanax. You think I should? Or a Valium? But then I might fall asleep. On her, I mean. I might not be able to come. Or to make her come. Then the whole thing would be a disaster."

"Well, Cassie likes you."

"Oh, she's cute, but she's not my type. Besides, she lives right in my neighborhood. It might spoil things with Karen. Then Karen would get pissed and move out and I'd be a nervous wreck again, like I was after Tess left. Come to think of it, maybe I'll just go back alone. I feel like I'm getting too old to keep engaging in this search for ecstasy. It's always so futile and so incredibly disappointing."

I gave her two tens and told her it looked like a skunk had died on her feet. She urged me to go to hell, as quickly as possible. That was okay. We were old friends and loved each other. Dell was the epitome of a bottom: she'd fight to be the one on her back. It was all fine and dandy with me—there was nothing like sex between us, anyway. But I couldn't figure out what she and Cassie would ever possibly do with each other in bed, assuming they made it that far, except lie side by side, full of wishes and unfulfilled desire. When she wandered off another slow song started—obviously the deejay was thinking about winding things down. I didn't ask this time but gestured, in a courtly way that made Cassie giggle, bending slightly at the waist, sweeping one arm grandly toward the dance floor. Around us, couples clutched in the beginnings of loss or passion, energy ebbing, fatigue settling softly like extra weight in the shadows and smoke. She cupped a hand to my ear.

"Want to fuck?"

"Yes, Cassie. But I like to say when, okay?"

As I said it, I realized it was true. And, as I realized that, I gained all kinds of power. Moving her in slow effortless circles and steps, dancing felt easy for the first time ever. I sensed her melting in against me, and held both of us up, moving, while my insides began to ache and burn.

At her place later, after the first time, she showed me all about bubble baths. I'd rarely bothered with stuff like that before—I was strictly a shower jock, stepping out of and into towels and steady hot modulated streams; and, I told her, the gypsies had a saying about baths, which they deemed an untrustworthy and inferior way to get clean: Why should I soak like an old tea bag? But Cassie's tub was different. Deep, aged, worn but clean, sunk like unmovable stone in the tiniest room of her tiny apartment, something about it felt seductive. Sinking into bubbles there was like sinking into a cloud, a pillow, a woman. She sat primly on the polished wood toilet seat, frayed satiny robe clutched protectively over both breasts, as if we hadn't just spent the past several hours making love—first shyly, then unrestrained raw fucking, then sweating close up against each other, and then again shy.

She was great, and made a big fuss about everything: the mixture of bubbles and lotions had to be just right, the washcloth her best, expensive skin creams were arrayed on shelves, waiting. I was touched by all this delicate consideration. It wasn't love—at least, not yet—but pleasing her had been exciting, and, now, I couldn't keep my hands off. When I stepped out dripping fragrant foams, she toweled different parts of me gently.

"I like your body."

"Yeah?"

"I like how strong you are."

I wanted to tell her that physical strength wasn't the same as a big, grown strength inside. But it occurred to me that maybe it was—a corresponding strength, at least, to the extent that it tangibly represented the fruits of work and a kind of courage—and, considering this silently, I reconsidered myself. That I even liked what I saw, not just tolerated it, but got some pleasure out of it as well—this image of her and me together in an age-speckled mirror—was wonderful. Something in me started to want, then, in a different, deeper way. I wondered if I'd let her make love to me some time. Not just as a tender femme service, the after-dinner drink on our sexual menu, but in a way that was scary, penetrative, requiring real trust and release. That—that was what she wanted, from the start: to be gotten deep inside of, to give up all control. I was glad of it. At the same time, I could barely imagine submitting or surrendering myself that way and calling it pleasure.

We were very different.

I dried my hands to light another cigarette and gave it over to her. She blew smoke in the direction of the mirror. In that moment she seemed very far away, exotic, her otherness electrifying. We started to kiss and touch again. Then she was lying on her open robe, on the bed, with me full on top of her. Bubble bath soaked into sheets. She had all the right playthings, Cassie did, and plenty of latex and lube— tricks of the trade, she said, smiling in a half-hard, half-sad way. Old massage parlor girls never show up unprepared, but then again, neither did I. If I shut my eyes against her hair, touched yielding flesh, it seemed as if the bed spun round and round.

I started to fall hard then, and wanted to move all the way inside her where the world's sharp edges were muted and soft. Wanted to push in rhythm with a deep, dark, strapped-on weight that would strain her and please her, invade on invitation, a burden we both could feel, then let go of, until it brought us to some unforsaken place of home and finality and love.

What happened: We became lovers, Cassie and I. A home, lace curtains, white picket fence, apple pie in the oven on Sundays—we had all that eventually, yes, but we had it in city rooms and clubs and streets, within ourselves and each other. And, inside, there was lots more too. Dyke stuff, tough and sweet. Things that cannot be described.

No one would let us adopt kids, so we took in homeless cats and dogs and, when everyone around us started dying, we cared for them in their illness, took in their cats and dogs after death, wept at many funerals. Another vomit-soaked sponge. Another kiss good-bye. Ceremonial washing of the hands. Bouquets of roses, incense, memorial speeches, listening over and over again to the favorite poems of dead young men. Afterwards, I'd walk her home in the dark. Protective. As if her electric femme-ness was a fragile thing instead of the sure gut-deep strength it was, too good for the hard straight world around us. As if I were more than a woman myself, a fiercely muscular giant, stronger than most men.

There is a darkness inside us, and also a light. And sometimes, both are wicked; and, sometimes, both are love. What Cassie taught me, after the bath, was that pain is not the same as suffering. We can have our sorrows and use them well, not just gyrate desperately to get rid of them. We can reach in and give and take. Reach in, or out, and be taken.

Reaching in is what I did with Cassie, my woman, on many, many nights. As time went by I let her reach deep inside of me, too—oh, not often, mind you, maybe once or twice a year, like I was giving her a gift she knew to treat carefully—and she'd touch something grieving then, a darkness, a womb-tip or star. Later we'd lie glued with sweating skin. Different bodies. Different fears. And, in this age of plague, we got over each drop of our shame. We learned to use our pain. We forbade nothing and accepted all. Until straight people everywhere began to imitate us. Then they grew to full human stature, and together we saved the world.

L'chiam, mi vida

SANDRA LEE GOLVIN

I watch the cigarette dangle like an invitation from the corner of her mouth and that exquisite butch style copped from Brando or James Dean makes me want to throw my body in front of her car and pray for a shocking death. I think it would suit her, to see me splayed under her tires murmuring final words of want in a bloody pulp of ecstasy. It's a certain Cuban Catholic sensibility I've acquired over the years of loving her, the exquisite escalation of the ancient guilt that is my Jewish birthright to sublime self-flagellation. So much more satisfying to actually be able to see the wound—run a finger along the scar tissue, a genuine map of the wounding, the sensate savagery in full occupation of the body—than to carry the evidence, invisible and unnameable, in the shadow tunnel of the psyche.

She hikes up her slate-blue sharkskin slacks cuffed like knives above her black wingtips, and runs a comb through her slicked-back silver hair. Then she grabs my pinky and threatens: "What if I break your finger?" Maybe I don't have to kill myself after all. Maybe this is the day she'll finally do it for me, break every part of my body she's ever promised to snap, rend me limb by limb in a frenzy of passionate desire. "It's like when you're little," my farm-girl lover explains, "and someone gives you a baby chick to hold, and you've got it cupped in your hands and it's so sweet you can't stand it so you just have to squeeze it to death." Oh yes, I will gladly offer myself up to the deadly caress of her fine hands whose sure stroke has taken me to the other side—heaven and hell—more times than I dare to count.

Years ago, after our first date, I dreamed about her arms. I was at a party and she entered in tight jeans, black boots and a man's white shirt, sleeves rolled back to reveal the biceps. I watched her cruise the crowd, nod to the other butches, wink at the pretty girls. As I sat waiting for her to come to me, I pointed in her direction and stated, "I want a woman with arms like hers." Giant muscular arms, strong enough to hold me down. I needed that force to contain me, the force of those arms hard as slabs of stone.

She taught me how to wrestle. Threw me on the bed and shoved me. "What are you, a sissy?" she asked, pushing at my chest. "Don't hurt me," I whined, not meaning it. "What's wrong with you? Don't you know how to fight?" No, I didn't. Not with my body, anyway. In my family you fought with language, words that could cut to the bone. When we needed to play, we played tennis. Contact sports were out. Not in her house. She was reared on football, dreamed of being a quarterback. She could be tackled without warning anywhere anytime and had to be prepared to stand her ground. Her big brother showed her the holds, how to throw your weight around, slither out from under someone larger than yourself. Now it was her turn to show me. I was her willing pupil.

She straddled my hips, pinned my arms above my head, pressed into me and challenged, "Now, get out of this." I struggled like a girl, without conviction. She tightened her hold on my wrists, a gleam in her eye. "C'mon baby," she coaxed softly, her rough voice only making me weaker. "I'm not letting you go." She meant it as a threat but it was what I wanted to hear. I threw off her hands and grabbed her black hair in my fists, holding her face next to mine. "Promise?" I asked, proud of finally meeting her in this taboo place. She smiled at her good little student, brought her arms quickly through mine to break the hold, and pulled my wrists down under my ass. Grinding the full weight of her muscled body into mine, she breathed into my ear: "Promise."

Several thousand nights later, she pins me again, though now I fight fiercely before I lose. Satisfied, she lies on her side next to me on the blood-colored cashmere carpet in the living room I painted vulva pink. Head in her right hand, she contemplates my chest. "I'm going to cut this out," she whispers, pointing at the place just over my left tit. "I have to do it before you do it to me," she nods. "That's what they taught us about you Jews. How you'll tempt us with your sexy pagan ways, then when we're not looking you'll cut out our hearts and eat them." Catholics have such vivid imaginations. I am thrilled. Maybe today will be the day she finally takes me to my death. I'll go happy. Completely owned.

virgin's gift
ROBIN BERNSTEIN

Anat skipped school again today. I know she's waiting for me on the roof of the movie theatre, chalking Hebrew obscenities in the tar and watching the traffic below. I know she's waiting for me.

"Hey, Baby, what took you so long?"

That's what she'll ask, if I meet her on the roof. I'll pull myself over the rail, rust from the fire escape streaking my hands and face. Before I can even wipe the dirt away, though, Anat will whip my long hair out of my face and kiss my lips. Kiss them deep. And then demand more.

But I'm not going to the roof, at least not yet. I'm going to Rosenbloom's Jewish Books and Religious Articles. To buy Anat a present.

My sneakers beat a rhythm on the sidewalk as questions pound through my head. Who is this girl who thrust herself into my life only a few weeks ago? Why should I buy her a present, when she bosses me around, makes fun of my lack of experience, and never answers a direct question? My answers also resound in rhythm: I'll buy her a present to make her miss Israel less, so she'll be less moody—and less likely to take it out on me. I'll buy her a present to apologize for not sleeping with her yet. To bribe her to wait for me. To make her want me even more.

A bell jingles when I open the door to Rosenbloom's. The Hasid at the counter looks up at me, then immediately looks away. For a moment I feel rude in my jeans and grungy turtleneck—hardly yeshiva-girl regulation. There's something in the Bible about women not wearing pants, like you're not supposed to confuse the genders or something. The Hasid's contempt is almost palpable. *Screw you,* I think, *I'm just as Jewish as you are. I've got as much right to be here.* Well, maybe I don't. It is his store.

I want to buy Anat something cute, like a Hebrew picture book or stencil set or refrigerator magnet or something. But I get distracted by the silver in the locked glass cases: heavy, shining candlesticks; ornate little boxes with hinged lids; menorahs whose graceful, twisting tines resemble flame itself, frozen mid-flicker. The weight of each piece crushes ridges into the velvet shelves. A Hasidic woman is behind me, digging through a trough of yarmulkes. She is in her thirties, wearing a soft, sacklike hat, calf-length blue skirt, and white tights like every other Hasidic woman I've ever seen. She picks up a yarmulke, inspects it from all sides, tugs the seams, peers, sneers, and tosses it back. She already has six or seven in her fist: one sedate black disk and a bunch of bright pre-school size yarmulkes with logos from football teams and Sesame Street. I wonder how many sons she has. I wonder who her husband is.

Suddenly, my mouth and eyes are wet. *It must be so easy,* I think. Longing splashes all over me, sudden as thunder and rain. To be this Hasidic woman, to have my life set: husband, sons, buying yarmulkes on a Wednesday afternoon. So easy. So clear. She doesn't have to ghost her way through high school, laboring each day to remain as inconspicuous as possible. She's not so lonely that she'll settle for anyone—even a sullen semi-delinquent who thinks all Americans are idiots—just to have someone to talk to. She would never be on her knees in gratitude, buying a girl a present just so she'll stick around. And when this Hasidic woman has sex—which she does, and I don't—she does it in a clean bed with the door closed. Not on a dirty roof with the sun beating down.

Oh, you're idealizing, I chide myself. She probably works twenty hours a day, boiling chickens and wiping baby butts. And what if she's lesbian, too? Imagine how awful that would be, to have to marry some guy or lose your whole community.

But maybe she's never even heard of lesbians. Then, maybe, it wouldn't be so bad. Would I be able to imagine women together, if I'd never heard the words? Maybe I'd think I was just shy or asexual. Maybe it would even be sort of okay.

I imagine myself, Hasidic, in bed, waiting for my husband. He pulls back the covers and climbs in—

No. The fantasy doesn't work; I'm cold as the silver behind the glass. I can't have this life even in dreams.

The Hasidic woman has noticed my stare; she's sizing me up me out of the corner of her eye. I move to the racks of tallises: dazzling white linen with silk embroidery, dark stripes and soft fringes. They have so much.

What if she is straight? I look at the Hasidic woman again. Imagine how wonderful that would be, to share desire with one person, over and over. I guess some Hasidic women don't love their husbands. But imagine being one of the ones who does. Imagine wanting your husband, never worrying about whether it was right or normal or if you were really sure or if you might change your mind. Never worrying about what anyone might think; knowing that everyone—family, friends, neighbors, rabbi, God Himself—was urging every kiss, every moan, every tremor in your hips. Imagine wanting your husband, wanting him, only him. And having him, over and over, year after year. Limitless.

I imagine myself not only Hasidic, but straight. Touching my husband, clinging to him, opening myself to him—

No. It still doesn't work. I can't enter this image, can't access this joy. So many people have it, and I never will.

I turn to the racks of books. I can always lose myself in words, in that march of black letters across white pages. Regular and fixed.

But these books offer no such escape. The books in these racks are heavy, bound in soft leather and stamped in gold. I can't read the Hebrew, but I know they're prayer books. Or Talmud. Or other stuff so holy I've never even heard of it. Heavy, beautiful books over which men run loving fingers, straining their eyes and pursing their murmuring lips. Books that are cherished, held and kissed, protected and praised. I wish someone would hold me, bless me, open me, read me, love me as each of these books will be. Each of these racks and racks of books that never need to be anything but what they are.

And I wish I could love these books the way the men do. Anat could read these pages, but I don't think she could tremble with them, cry as I've seen men cry. She doesn't care about religion, probably wouldn't be impressed by the soft leather covers and gold-rimmed leaves.

I'm tired of being unimpressed, of not caring. I wish love would flow out of me like it flows from the quaking men in synagogue. I wish I believed in God. I wish I could love leather-bound books and God with all my soul, with all my passion, with no hesitancy or self-consciousness or shame. I wish I could love a girl with my heart and my eyes and my lips; a girl who'd accept my love without laughing at me or calling me a stupid American virgin or wanting to pound my hips into the tar on a filthy roof. I wish I could love easily, fully, three times a day in synagogue and every night in a clean bed with my wife—

I stop short. *My wife?* That's not what I meant. Wives are for—

I grab a book and leaf through it, trying to remember my Hebrew alphabet, trying to recognize a word or two, trying to concentrate. Trying to push away the idea that has already exploded into countless streaks of light like fireworks and now buzzes toward me from every direction, unavoidable—

If I were a man.

If I were a man. A Hasid. I could love my wife, over and over, year after year, limitless.

I almost put the book down and run from the store. *Oh no,* I think, *does this mean I'm a transsexual? Please, please,* I pray to a god I don't believe in, *not that. I have so many problems already.*

But the idea still pulses through me, the image of myself as a Hasid. Loving a woman over and over, with all the blessings of the fathers.

I turn again to the Hasidic woman. She has finished selecting yarmulkes and has migrated toward the cash register. I imagine myself touching her, knowing she has never been touched by any man—not at all, not even a handshake—other than her husband. Knowing her breasts—her stomach, her shoulders, maybe even her *wrists*—have never been seen by any man except her husband. Imagining myself as that husband, imagining a woman so honoring me. Sharing her body with me, only me, forever.

But this woman is not my type. She's as old as my mother, for one thing. And her hands are full of yarmulkes for her husband. There is no room for me in that bed. I need my own wife to love.

I rush to a rack of lucite key rings with women's names. My wife must have a name. ("My wife"—the thought still terrifies me, but I will not think now about what it might mean.) I flip through the plastic tags: Yocheved, Malka, Ruchel—I don't like these names. What are the Hasidic girls on my block called? Gitti, Shoshana, Chanie—that's the one. But not Chanie. Chana. My wife is named Chana.

My wife.

Chana.

The wedding guests are still dancing, men waving bottles of wine and schnapps on one side of the hall, women on the other side weaving through circles of dance and gossip. My father and uncles pushed me into a chair, then raised it above their heads and bounced me toward the ceiling to the sound of accordions and fiddles. After the women did the same with Chana, my parents and her parents were also danced through the air. Then my father brought me another shot of schnapps and told me to leave the party. My time had come.

So now I am home with my Chana. Now I am in the bedroom I will share always with Chana.

A man is not supposed to look at a woman unless she is his wife. As a boy, of course, I looked into the faces of my mother and sisters. But as I grew older, I learned to look at the ground or at other men when women passed. In moments of weakness I have snuck quick glances—haven't we all?—but I have never held a woman's gaze. Now, for the first time, I may look. Without fear. Without shame. For as long as I want. Without pretending to do otherwise. Without disguising my passion.

Her eyes are as hungry as mine; her gaze darts over every point of my face. Unmarried women must keep a distance from men as well, if they want to retain respect. But now, we may both look, and we do, we do.

And my eyes...how can I see so much at once? Her long face, full lips, soft gray eyes—so much to see. The vast expanse of skin from forehead to chin, from nose to ear on each side. So much exposed. So much softness. And I will touch that softness tonight, and over and over for the rest of my life. I am weak with unbelieving.

She removes the veil covering the top of her head, and her curly hair falls down. As a married woman, she will cover her hair in public from now on, but she will not shave her head as women used to. We are a modern people. Chana's black curls tumble around her face; the smell of shampoo drifts toward me.

For a moment, my amazement is displaced by panic. Who is this woman who has been thrust into my life? Ours was not purely an arranged marriage; we have spoken several times and consented to each other. But one could not say we know each other well. Perhaps we should not touch tonight, but instead talk.

Chana has noticed the distraction in my eyes; questions and disappointment fog her face.

I push my hesitancies aside. Tomorrow we will talk. We have the expanse of our whole lives to get to know each other. Tonight we must fulfill our obligation to each other, not as individuals but as man and woman, husband and wife. Tonight, we exist only to satisfy each other's desire, as we have been commanded.

Without thinking, I reach out my hand to her. She raises her hand, and lays a single finger in my palm. We sit on the bed together, the pad of her finger slowly tracing lines in my palm. I am transfixed on her finger, on skin touching skin. Somehow, I never believed I could really be so lucky. I never thought this would actually happen to me.

I close my hand around her finger and press hard. I hear her breath catch and I look up, concerned that I have hurt her. But her lips are parted, eyes half-closed, cheeks flush.

The sight ignites me so. I grab both her hands in mine, and without even thinking, I am kissing them, rubbing my lips feverishly against her palms, licking the cracks between her fingers.

Chana is moaning now. I take each manicured finger full in my mouth, sucking hard. She rakes her nails through my beard. I lick, suck, bite, breathe hot over her wrists, feel her pulse through my lips. Chana is gasping now and maybe I am, too. I slide off the bed and kneel before her, hugging her hands to the sides of my head, blocking out our sounds. It's too much. I can't take it all in one night.

But Chana will not let me escape. Still in her wedding gown, she slides off the bed and kneels beside me on the floor. The dress rustles as if layers hide beneath the skirt.

My hands still clap hers tight to the sides of my head. But suddenly, she takes control and pulls my face toward hers. And Chana, my Chana, kisses me full on the lips.

Oh, so many times I have praised God, so many nights I have recited the shma, the call to all Jews on Earth. *Shma Yisroel Adonai Elohenu Adonai Echad*—Hear, oh Israel, the Lord is God, the Lord is One. But only when Chana's soft lips meet mine, when I taste her breath and feel the flicker of her tongue—only then, for the first time, do I feel my spirit burst from my body to touch all others. Only this joyful noise could reach all on earth. This kiss is the shma—hear oh Israel, this kiss is God, and we are one. Chana and I. And all Jews, shma, all breathing creatures on the earth, shma, all kisses, shma, are one.

We fall to the floor.

Chana is in my arms and we are rolling. I'm so happy, I start to laugh. For a moment, she looks confused, then she laughs, too, grabbing me tighter as we roll on the carpet. It feels so good, this squeezing. All these years of not being touched; now I press her hard against my chest, kissing and laughing, rolling and gazing and laughing for a long, long time.

But suddenly, through our laughter, I become aware of her breasts pressing against my chest like two soft biscuits. And my laughter dissolves.

Something serious sweeps through me—a new kind of grave desire incinerating my bones, my flesh, my thinking mind. My laughter is gone; I hold Chana tense, my eyes inches from hers. And she stops laughing, too.

"Chana," I say, my voice so smoked with desire that I barely recognize it. "Chana," I say, "Please take off your dress."

She is still for a moment. Her eyes close once, then open to me. She kisses me once more, quickly, on my lips. And then she pulls away.

"Yes," she says, and the word sounds like a single drop of rain sliding off a leaf. "Yes, I will take off my dress for you."

And wonder of wonder, it happens. Chana stands without breaking my gaze. Watching my eyes, she reaches around to her own back in such a way I did not know arms could bend. And she slowly unzips her wedding gown. Then she loosens the cuffs around her wrists. And slowly, as if by magic, the dress sinks to the floor. The white dress is heaped around Chana's ankles, like clouds at the feet of God. I am worshipping.

Do all women have so much skin beneath their clothes? The thought is incredible, obscene. No wonder men and women are separated so strictly; what man could concentrate enough to tie his own shoes with women hovering about, naked and entrancing, hidden only by thin sheaths of cloth?

But now I do not need to concentrate on anything but my Chana, who stands before me in white underpants and a brassiere. Chana, with the bony, pale shoulders, the impossible softness tucked into her brassiere, the small roundness of her belly.

"And you?" she whispers.

"What?"

"My husband," she says, "take off your suit."

For a moment, I am shocked. In anticipation of this night, I had imagined touching Chana, imagined us pushing together beneath the covers. But it never occurred to me that I might undress in front of her. I am suddenly sheepish. My clothes will not curl gracefully from my body as hers did from her; I doubt I could muster the power to stand unclothed and commanding as she. I cannot equal her, can never be as beautiful for her as she is for me. Her beauty is a gift I must accept humbly, knowing I can never return it.

But she is my wife. And she is right. I must satisfy her tonight. And she wants me naked before her. So be it.

I stumble to my feet and begin tugging at my shirt. My fingers, so sensitive a moment ago, now struggle. It's as if the buttons have turned to mist; I can't grip them. But finally I release myself. The trousers are easier; they unzip like Chana's dress. I kick them aside.

I stand in my underwear, undershirt, and tallis. Do I take off the prayer shawl? I suppose I must. I lift it off gingerly, suppressing an urge to flick the fringes against her belly. I fold my tallis neatly on the nightstand.

"Undershirt, too," she says. There is no graceful way to obey; I yank the shirt over my head.

And we stand, three feet of air pulsing between us. She gapes at the hair on my chest—is it enough? is it too much? I worry—and on my stomach. I feel each hair spring to life and reach toward her, like the fur on a jungle cat's back.

And Chana, my Chana, moves toward me.

But she stops, inches away. I can see every pore, every freckle on her shoulders. She smells like soap and wine and something else I've never smelled before. I want her all at once, hot and electric, inside and outside, I want her so badly, now and forever, I want her so, I almost cry with the wanting. I almost fall to my knees and cry. No one has ever before had such power over me; at this moment, I would trade my soul, sell myself into bondage for her. And at the same time, my desire could burst from my body, grip her, deliver her to me like a wave crashing on the shore. I am a king about to ravage a feast. I am a boy afraid to taste the wine.

I move not at all.

Slowly, sighing, Chana folds herself into me. First she touches her bare shoulder to mine. Then she rolls her bosom against my chest. And her silken hands slide to my back.

So much warm skin against skin.

My hands travel her spine. And the curls of her hair.

Now our kisses come fast, forceful. I kiss through the softness of our lips, into the hardness of her teeth and bone. My fingers press into not just skin, but muscles and joints. I push and she falls, we fall, into the bed.

The front of my shorts stands like a pyramid. Now. "Now," I say, and bump my clumsy hands against her breasts. I tear at the fabric separating her from me. I must be rid of it. But the fabric clings to her.

"It's—" Chana's breath is as rushed as mine. "It's in back," she says. "The clasp."

I grip the back panel and pull, but nothing opens. Chana throws off my hands, then reaches behind her (again with that arm-breaking contortion) and unbuckles herself. And like the dress before, the brassiere melts off her body.

Oh, her breasts are small and soft; her nipples brown and wrinkled and large in my hands, between my lips and my tongue like sweet raisins in challah. I kiss and lick every part of her, gnawing and kneading. I am on top of her, pressing myself between her legs. Chana is moaning; heat tumbles forth from her divide.

Suddenly, her hand darts down and grips me below, through the cotton of my underpants.

Never before have I been so touched, and I stop, shocked, simply feeling her fingers around me.

"Please," she says. "Now. Please." Her fingers find my elastic waistband. And they slide beneath to grip me again.

I am motionless, gape-mouthed, wordless. Her dry, warm hand travels up and down my length, burrowing into the thicket below. Her other hand tugs my underwear to my knees.

"Now," she says, withdrawing her hand to strip off her underpants as well. I grab her buttocks in my hands, crash her body against mine, kiss frantically, swipe my palms against her drenched hairiness. My greatest sensitivity is extending, extending toward hers. With a gasp, I push my sensitivity into her wetness, where all is warm and dark and plump and throbbing alive. Oh, my sensitivity is in hers and we are rocking in and out, throbbing to throbbing, crying and spilling and oh, I am buried so deep, my whole body vaults to press deeper into her heat. Then we are rubbing faster, sweat and tears and slickness pouring off us.

Chana screams and arches first, shuddering over and over and clutching my shoulders. And then the world turns red and yellow and pink and I empty into her, each pulse sweeter and sweeter and sweeter, until there is no more. No more but sweat and warmth, and Chana in my arms.

I am suddenly aware that I am still standing—slack-mouthed, vacant-eyed, wet-crotched—in Rosenbloom's Jewish Books and Religious Articles.

My eyes focus forward on a shelf of small cardboard containers.

Shabbos candles, twelve to a box.

Anat. I remember: I came here to buy a present for Anat. And I have chosen the gift I will bring to her roof, the gift I will give with desire and certainty.

I will give Anat these wax sticks and say, "When I love a woman for the first time, it will be slow, on a clean bed, with red wine, by candlelight." I will watch her eyes. And then I will walk away.

I take my candles to the Hasid behind the cash register. As he gives me my change, I notice he is careful not to touch my hand.

ROBIN BERNSTEIN

Against

Chrystos

your skin red under my hand against every
political principle we both hold you want
me to spank you & I do
We're survivors of childhood violence with black eyes
in common from mothers who hated our difference
Neither loves our love
they'd beat it out of us if they could
Your people as well as mine slaughtered in millions
Queer we're still open season
My fingermarks on your ass are loving you
tied to the bed my other hand pushing
in our vortex of pleasure   I'd agree that it's wrong
to do this
Out of our bruised lives should come some other way
This forbidden hand this deep memory this connection
for which I've no explanation against a wall of right
that would define us as victim/aggressor
I want to give you
what you want
although my kind would beat it out of me with words
if they could
My hands guess this is a difference that is a crime
to admit in our small queer world
Desire red & raw as wounds we disguise
we're open season

188   CHRYSTOS

about the authors

DONNA ALLEGRA'S writing is anthologized in *Sportsdykes, Lesbian Erotics, All the Way Home, Queer View Mirror, Dyke Life, My Lover Is a Woman, Lesbian Short Fiction,* and the forthcoming *Close Calls* and *The Wild Good: Lesbian Photographs & Writings on Love.*

KATYA ANDREEVNA'S erotic fiction has appeared in *Heatwave: Women in Love and Lust, Once Upon a Time: Erotic Fairy Tales for Women, The New Worlds of Women,* and *Best American Erotica 1996.*

LAURA ANTONIOU is in recovery from compulsive publishing syndrome, taking a break from the hectic four-books-a-year schedule she has kept for three years. The author of *The Marketplace* series of novels and editor of an assortment of anthologies is now spending time writing for other anthologies and working on various secret projects all bound to come out in the same year.

RED JORDAN AROBATEAU is a butch dyke and author of forty self-published dyke novels, many of which have been republished by Masquerade Books, including *Lucy and Mickey, Dirty Pictures, Boys Night Out,* and *Rough Trade.* She was given the written word as a weapon to fight injustice in the world. She fought for her stories and she fought to tell them.

ROBIN BERNSTEIN co-edited *Generation Q,* an anthology of essays by queers born after the Stonewall Riots. Her writing appears in over twenty periodicals and many books, including *Dyke Strippers* and

Eating Our Hearts Out. A former associate editor of *The Washington Blade,* she is currently an editor of *Bridges: A Journal for Jewish Feminists and Our Friends.* "Virgin's Gift" is an excerpt from her novel-in-progress, *Tammy Wexler Needs Your Help!.*

BETH BRANT is a Bay of Quinte Mohawk from Tyendinaga Mohawk Territory in Ontario. She is the editor of the groundbreaking collection of work by Native women, *A Gathering of Spirit,* and *I'll Sing Til the Day I Die.* She is the author of *Mohawk Trail, Food and Spirits,* and *Writing as Witness.* Her writing has appeared in over seventy anthologies throughout the world. She is currently at work on a book of essays and a novel.

CHRYSTOS is a widely acclaimed writer and Native Rights activist. Her collections of poetry include *Fire Power, Fugitive Colors,* and *In Her I Am.* She won the Audre Lorde International Poetry Competition in 1994, and the Sappho Award of Distinction from the Astraea National Lesbian Action Foundation in 1995.

CHERYL CLARKE is an African-American, lesbian-feminist poet and author of four books of poetry: *Narratives: Poems in the Tradition of Black Women, Living as a Lesbian, Humid Pitch,* and *Experimental Love,* which was nominated for a 1994 Lambda Award for Poetry. Her poems, essays and book reviews have appeared in numerous publications, including: *This Bridge Called My Back, Home Girls, Inversions, The Persistent Desire, Feminist Studies* and *The Black Scholar.* She currently directs the Office of Diverse Community Affairs at Rutgers University, where she is also pursuing a doctorate in African-American literature.

BREE COVEN originated the Baby Dyke column "Hey, Baby!" for *Deneuve* (now *Curve*) magazine, where she was a regular contributor for three years. Her poetry, essays and smut appear in *The Femme Mystique, Generation Q: Inheriting Stonewall, Pucker Up, Princess Magazine,* and the forthcoming *Motherlies.* Bree lives in New York where she is studying writing at Sarah Lawrence College and working on a book about S/M as a means of recovery from childhood sexual abuse.

JEANNINE DELOMBARD'S essays have appeared in *Dyke Life* and *To Be Real.* Her book reviews and feature articles have appeared in *The New York Times Book Review, Out, The Philadelphia Inquirer,* and *The Philadelphia City Paper.* "Steam" is her first piece of erotic fiction.

MARÍA HELENA DOLAN knows that all roads—as well as intergalactic coordinates—lead to Atlanta. Labeled the "Mouth of the South" by *Out* magazine, she lives among cultivated tropical fecundity with felines who harbor schemes for total global domination. She's making the trains run on time as well as writing a novel.

SANDRA LEE GOLVIN is a native Los Angelena, queer cultural activist, dyke poet and lawyer. S/he is published in the anthologies *Hers, Ritual Sex,* and *Best Lesbian Erotica 1996,* and the journals *Fireweed, Pucker Up,* and *Spoon River Poetry Review.* S/he is the co-editor of the 'zine *Diabolical Clits.* Her critically acclaimed one-woman show, *Pumpkin Pie: A Story of Cross-Gender Transcendence,* ran at Highways as part of Ecce Lesbo/Ecce Homo, the Sixth Annual National Lesbian and Gay Performance Festival. Her thing is gender, language, and the belief in magic.

KAREN GREEN'S work appears in *Best Lesbian Erotica 1996, Boji for the Mentally Ill, Princess, Pucker Up,* the forthcoming anthology *Forbidden: Defiant New Lesbian Fiction,* and dozens of self-published volumes. She is currently working on *A Girl's Guide to Taking Over the World: Writing from the Girl Zine Revolution,* with her cohort and concubine, Tristan Taormino. She works as a graphic designer and co-promotes the swinging new dyke club, Club Xanadu, in the East Village. She's at work on her second novel, *The Wall of Unsaid Things,* from which her story is an excerpt.

RAVEN B. KALDERA is a pansexual writer, astrologer, and priest/ess of the Dark Goddess with a beautiful partner/wife and one daughter. Raven has work in the Circlet Press anthologies *S/M Futures, S/M Pasts, Blood Kiss, Fetish Fantastic,* and *The New Worlds of Women,* as well as the forthcoming anthologies *Make Mama Happy, Butch Tops, Bitch Goddesses,* and *Leather Spirit.*

MELISSA KLEIN is originally from Washington, D.C. and moved to San Francisco in 1995 with her cat Addison, whom she feared would exceed the carry-on baggage weight limit on the airplane. Since moving to San Francisco, she has taught creative writing to high school students for whom English is a second language. She also works with homeless and runaway youth on HIV prevention. She sporadically produces the 'zine *Inkling,* when she's not distracted by her penchant for donuts and bad television.

MICKEY LASKIN is a New York City-based teacher, writer, musician, and member of the Lesbian Sex Mafia. Her writing career began in academia and journalism, but while enduring a year of unrequited love and lust, she began "writing sex," thereby transforming her sexual frustrations into virtual orgasms, which she shares with her readers. Her queer fiction, essays, and journalism have been published in *Venus Infers, Bad Attitude,* and *Prometheus,* and her fiction appears (sometimes under the pseudonym Maria Santiago) in anthologies including *Heatwave: Women in Love and Lust, The Second Coming,* and *Leatherwomen III.*

JENIFER LEVIN is the author of four novels: *Water Dancer* (nominated for the PEN/Hemingway First Novel Award), *Snow, Shimoni's Lover,* and *The Sea of Light* (nominated for a Lambda Fiction Award), and a short story collection, *Love and Death, and Other Disasters.* She has written for *The New York Times, The Washington Post, Rolling Stone, Ms., Mademoiselle, Forward, The Advocate, The Harvard Gay and Lesbian Review,* and many other publications. Her short fiction is widely anthologized. She lives in New York City with her partner and their children.

HEATHER LEWIS is the author of *House Rules,* which won the Ferro-Grumley Award, the New Voice Award, was a Lambda Literary Award finalist, and has been optioned for a film. Her fiction has appeared in *Living with the Animals* and *Surface Tension.* She's at work on a new novel that will be published by Doubleday.

VICKI LEWIS grew up in the middle of Tennessee. She now lives in San Francisco, where she is growing too big for her breeches. "The Pond" is her first published work.

DAWN MILTON is a native Westerner doing time in New York City. The renegade lesbian daughter of a Born-Again cowboy, she is presently working on her Ph.D. dissertation on the religious right.

CHERRÍE MORAGA is a poet, playwright, and essayist. Some of her works include *Loving in the War Years, This Bridge Called My Back: Writings by Radical Women of Color, Shadow of a Man, The Last Generation,* and *Heroes and Saints.* She has won numerous awards for her plays and poetry including the Before Columbus American Book Award, the Fund for New American Plays Award, and the National Endowment for the Arts Theatre Playwrights' Fellowship.

KATHLEEN E. MORRIS, from Brooklyn, New York, is a double Libra (with Gemini rising) Buddhist BAP (Black-American Princess). Author of *Speaking in Whispers: African-American Lesbian Erotica,* she identifies herself as a militant total-femme dyke. She is on the board of directors of the Astraea National Lesbian Action Foundation.

CAROL QUEEN is an erotic writer and cultural sexologist (working on a Ph.D. in human sexuality—you should see the lab work she has to do). She's at work on a novel (from which "Ariel" is an excerpt) called *The Leather Daddy and the Femme.* She is the author of *Exhibitionism for the Shy* and a forthcoming collection of essays *Real Live Nude Girl;* she also co-edited *Switch Hitters: Lesbians Write Gay Male Erotica and Gay Men Write Lesbian Erotica.*

CECILIA TAN is a writer, editor, and sexuality activist. She is a top, a bottom, a switch, a boy, a girl, and likes it that way. Her erotic fiction can be found in many publications including *Ms., Penthouse, Paramour, Sojourner, On A Bed of Rice, Switch Hitters, Herotica* 3, 4 and 5, and *Best American Erotica 1996.* She is the publisher and editor of Circlet Press, erotic science fiction and fantasy anthologies.

DOLPHIN JULIA TRAHAN is a Hawaiian haole living in San Francisco. She co-directs BUILD and is a featured performer in the documentary film *Vital Signs: Crip Culture Talks Back.* Her writing appears in *The Disability Studies Reader, Virgin Territory 2, Frighten the Horses, Sinister Wisdom, First Person Sexual,* and *Mouth: The Voice of Disability Rights.*

KITTY TSUI is the author of *Breathless,* which won the Firecracker Alternative Book Award in the sex category. Published in over fifty anthologies worldwide, she recently completed *Sparks Fly,* a book of gay male erotica under the pseudonym Eric Norton, forthcoming from Masquerade Books. She is at work on *Breathless Again.*

LAUREN VOLOSHEN was born feet-first in Pittsburgh in 1954, the year of *Brown v. Board of Education,* and she shares her birthday with Malcolm X, Ho Chi Mihn, and Grace Jones. As a grown-up journalist, she covered the transition from military dictatorship to so-called democracy in Guatemala and the Contra War in Nicaragua. Tired of chasing criminals and politicians, she turned to academics, poetry and fiction writing. She currently teaches at the University of Maryland while she pursues a Ph.D.

About the editors

JEWELLE GOMEZ is the author of *The Gilda Stories*, winner of two Lambda Literary Awards for fiction; *Forty-Three Septembers*, a collection of essays; and *Oral Tradition*, her third collection of poetry, all from Firebrand Books. Born in Boston, she lived in New York City for twenty-two years and is currently the Executive Director of the Poetry Center and American Poetry Archives at San Francisco State University.

TRISTAN TAORMINO is Publisher and Editrix of the pansexual erotic magazine *Pucker Up*. She is co-editor of *Ritual Sex*, a collection of writing on sex, religion, and spirituality. Her work appears in the anthologies *The Femme Mystique, Heatwave: Women in Love and Lust, Chick-Lit 2, Virgin Territory II,* and *Strategic Sex,* as well as *On Our Backs, The Advocate, X-X-X Fruit, Venus Infers,* and *Blue Blood*. She recently completed two anthologies: *Forbidden: Defiant New Lesbian Fiction* and *A Girl's Guide to Taking Over the World: Writing from the Girl Zine Revolution,* which she co-edited with her partner, Karen Green, forthcoming from St. Martin's Press.

Books from cleis press

SEXUAL POLITICS

Forbidden Passages:
Writings Banned in Canada,
introductions by Pat Califia
and Janine Fuller.
ISBN: 1-57344-019-1
14.95 paper.

Public Sex: The
Culture of Radical Sex
by Pat Califia.
ISBN: 0-939416-89-1
12.95 paper.

Sex Work: Writings by
Women in the Sex Industry,
edited by Frédérique
Delacoste and Priscilla
Alexander.
ISBN: 0-939416-11-5
16.95 paper.

Susie Bright's Sexual
Reality: A Virtual Sex
World Reader
by Susie Bright.
ISBN: 0-939416-59-X
9.95 paper.

Susie Bright's Sexwise
by Susie Bright.
ISBN: 1-57344-002-7
10.95 paper.

Susie Sexpert's Lesbian
Sex World
by Susie Bright.
ISBN: 0-939416-35-2
9.95 paper.

EROTIC LITERATURE

Best Gay Erotica 1997,
selected by Douglas Sadownick,
edited by Richard Labonté.
ISBN: 1-57344-067-1
14.95 paper.

Best Gay Erotica 1996,
selected by Scott Heim,
edited by Michael Ford.
ISBN: 1-57344-052-3
12.95 paper.

Best Lesbian Erotica 1997,
selected by Jewelle Gomez,
edited by Tristan Taormino.
ISBN: 1-57344-065-5
14.95 paper.

Best Lesbian Erotica 1996,
selected by Heather Lewis,
edited by Tristan Taormino.
ISBN: 1-57344-054-X
12.95 paper.

Serious Pleasure: Lesbian
Erotic Stories and Poetry,
edited by the Sheba
Collective.
ISBN: 0-939416-45-X
9.95 paper.

Switch Hitters: Lesbians
Write Gay Male Erotica
and Gay Men Write
Lesbian Erotica,
edited by Carol Queen
and Lawrence Schimel.
ISBN: 1-57344-021-3
12.95 paper.

GENDER TRANSGRESSION

Body Alchemy:
Transsexual Portraits
by Loren Cameron.
ISBN: 1-57344-062-0
24.95 paper.

Dagger: On Butch Women,
edited by Roxxie,
Lily Burana, Linnea Due.
ISBN: 0-939416-82-4
14.95 paper.

I Am My Own Woman:
The Outlaw Life of
Charlotte von Mahlsdorf,
translated by Jean Hollander.
ISBN: 1-57344-010-8
12.95 paper.

LESBIAN AND GAY STUDIES

The Case of the Good-For-Nothing Girlfriend
by Mabel Maney.
ISBN: 0-939416-91-3
10.95 paper.

The Case of the Not-So-Nice Nurse
by Mabel Maney.
ISBN: 0-939416-76-X
9.95 paper.

Nancy Clue and the Hardly Boys in A Ghost in the Closet
by Mabel Maney.
ISBN: 1-57344-012-4
10.95 paper.

A Lesbian Love Advisor
by Celeste West.
ISBN: 0-939416-26-3
9.95 paper.

On the Rails: A Woman's Journey, second edition,
by Linda Niemann.
Introduction
by Leslie Marmon Silko.
ISBN: 1-57344-064-7.
14.95 paper.

THRILLERS & DYSTOPIAS

Another Love
by Erzsébet Galgóczi.
ISBN: 0-939416-51-4
8.95 paper.

Dirty Weekend: A Novel of Revenge by Helen Zahavi.
ISBN: 0-939416-85-9
10.95 paper.

Only Lawyers Dancing
by Jan McKemmish.
ISBN: 0-939416-69-7
9.95 paper.

The Wall
by Marlen Haushofer.
ISBN: 0-939416-54-9
9.95 paper.

VAMPIRES & HORROR

Dark Angels: Lesbian Vampire Stories,
edited by Pam Keesey.
ISBN 1-7344-014-0
10.95 paper.

Daughters of Darkness: Lesbian Vampire Stories,
edited by Pam Keesey.
ISBN: 0-939416-78-6
9.95 paper.

Women Who Run with the Werewolves: Tales of Blood, Lust and Metamorphosis,
edited by Pam Keesey.
ISBN: 1-57344-057-4
12.95 paper.

Sons of Darkness: Tales of Men, Blood and Immortality,
edited by Michael Rowe and Thomas S. Roche.
ISBN: 1-57344-059-0
12.95 paper.

DEBUT NOVELS

Memory Mambo
by Achy Obejas.
ISBN: 1-57344-017-5
12.95 paper.

We Came All The Way from Cuba So You Could Dress Like This?: Stories
by Achy Obejas.
ISBN: 0-939416-93-X
10.95 paper.

Seeing Dell
by Carol Guess
ISBN: 1-57344-023-X
12.95 paper.

SEX GUIDES

The Good Vibrations Guide to Sex: How to Have Safe, Fun Sex in the '90s
by Cathy Winks
and Anne Semans.
ISBN: 0-939416-84-0
16.95 paper.

Good Sex: Real Stories from Real People,
second edition,
by Julia Hutton.
ISBN: 1-57344-000-0
14.95 paper.

COMIX

Dyke Strippers: Lesbian Cartoonists A to Z,
edited by Roz Warren.
ISBN: 1-57344-008-6
16.95 paper.

The Night Audrey's Vibrator Spoke: A Stonewall Riots Collection
by Andrea Natalie.
ISBN: 0-939416-64-6
8.95 paper.

Revenge of Hothead Paisan: Homicidal Lesbian Terrorist
by Diane DiMassa.
ISBN: 1-57344-016-7
16.95 paper.

TRAVEL & COOKING

Betty and Pansy's Severe Queer Review of San Francisco
by Betty Pearl and Pansy.
ISBN: 1-57344-056-6
10.95 paper.

Food for Life & Other Dish,
edited by Lawrence Schimel.
ISBN: 1-57344-061-2
14.95 paper.

WRITER'S REFERENCE

*Putting Out: The Essential
Publishing Resource Guide
For Gay and Lesbian
Writers,*
third edition,
by Edisol W. Dotson.
ISBN: 0-939416-87-5
12.95 paper.

*Women & Honor: Some
Notes on Lying*
by Adrienne Rich.
ISBN: 0-939416-44-1
3.95 paper.

Since 1980, Cleis Press publishes provocative books by women (and a few men) in the United States and Canada. We welcome your order and will ship your books as quickly as possible. Individual orders must be prepaid (U.S. dollars only). Please add 15% shipping. PA residents add 6% sales tax. Mail orders: Cleis Press, PO Box 8933, Pittsburgh PA 15221. MasterCard and Visa orders: include account number, exp. date, and signature. FAX your credit card order: (412) 937-1567. Or, phone us Mon-Fri, 9 am - 5 pm EST: (412) 937-1555 or (800) 780-2279.